METHODS OF VEGETATION STUDY

METHODS OF
VEGETATION
STUDY

EDWIN ALLEN PHILLIPS
Pomona College, Claremont Graduate School, and
University of Michigan Biological Station

HOLT, RINEHART AND WINSTON, INC.
NEW YORK, CHICAGO, SAN FRANCISCO, TORONTO, LONDON

27055–0119

Printed in the United States of America

65582

*To my
mother
and
father*

PREFACE

At present there is a great diversity of concepts and methods in vegetation study. This diversity is proper and characteristic of a young, vigorous, developing field of science, but it produces confusion, particularly to the beginning student.

One approach to the teaching of elementary ecology most generally followed is the concentration upon one system to avoid this confusion. This book takes the other approach, the simplified presentation of several different systems from the European continent, Great Britain, and America.

For research and travel funds I would like to express my appreciation to the trustees of Pomona College, to the Claremont Graduate School, and to the National Science Foundation.

Claremont, California   E.A.P.
January 5, 1959

CONTENTS

(Chapter 3 — continued)

INTRODUCTION

The field study of vegetation provides an excellent introduction to plant ecology, of which it is a part.

Kerner, one of the earliest of the plant ecologists, in 1863 wrote a book entitled "Pflanzenleben der Donauland" which includes the following:

Scarcely a hundredth part of the plants in a list contribute materially to the visible garment which spreads itself before us.

This quotation is the essence of the difference between the taxonomic and ecologic approach to plants. The taxonomist in studying an area makes a list of species which constitute the *flora*. The ecologist begins with the floristic list and by a series of sample plots or observations ascertains the quantitative and qualitative relationships of the various species in the flora, leading to a concept of the *vegetation*. This book is concerned with various methods of sampling and with the treatment of data thus gathered.

In Britain and America, ecology includes the study of individual organisms in relation to individual factors of the environment (autecology) and the study of groups of organisms or complexes of factors (synecology). In Europe the first of these is known as ecology and the second as plant sociology. This book is in the field of synecology, or plant sociology.

To the Instructor:

Obviously it is impossible for a class to do all of the exercises. The instructor has a wide latitude of choice, but it is suggested that some exercises be included from each part. Different combinations of the methods presented are possible and encouraged after the class understands the principles involved.

In the exercises, wherever appropriate in written work and tables, general observations concerning the sites investigated should be required. These may include location, soil type and other soil characteristics, elevation, slope, climate, animal factors, history, and other special features.

For elementary work an area of vegetation should be chosen that is homogeneous, with no abrupt or marked change in topography, slope, exposure, or species composition. It is also desirable over a period of years to keep records of some of the areas for comparisons and for checking the work of successive classes as well as for noting vegetational changes.

For many of the exercises it would be a decided advantage to have an extensive area in which complete data for all the vegetation is known. This facilitates the evaluation of different sampling methods. The area thus tallied can be increased by successive classes until it reaches useful size. Bormann (1953) made a complete enumeration of a five-acre oak-hickory stand in Duke University Forest which has proved very useful for method evaluation.

Literature cited appears as a section of the Bibliography. Another section includes a list of books and journals which should be available for general class use.

Although this book does not attempt to describe their use, whatever instruments are available for measuring environmental factors can be used and the results correlated with these exercises. A list of instruments used in these exercises, with descriptions where necessary, will be found in the Appendix.

METHODS OF VEGETATION STUDY

Part One

Preliminary Survey

CHAPTER 1 — MAPPING

In most vegetation studies it is desirable to locate an area in such a way that it may be relocated. Detailed maps of counties or smaller subdivisions are useful for gross locations which should include, where available, highway route numbers and miles and direction from nearest towns or other points. The goal is to make certain that new classes unfamiliar with the location will be able to find it.

More precise location can be accomplished with measuring tapes, Brunton-type compasses, and permanent stakes. If the study area is to be used for several years, it is often worth the time and effort to make a map, locating certain landmarks and prominent vegetation boundaries or large individual plants.

EXERCISE 1. Detailed location of an area from permanent objects

Before using this method for location of an area in the field, a class should become familiar with the use of the Brunton-type compass in the location of objects around the campus or even in corridors. Good directions are enclosed with the instruments.

With a little practice, students soon become familiar with this type of compass in which East and West seem to be reversed (see Figure 1). The scale reads from 0 to 360 degrees, with 0 degrees indicating north, 90 degrees indicating east, 180 degrees indicating south, and 270 degrees indicating west.

In use the compass is rotated until the weighted end of the needle is on the desired bearing – for example, on 90 degrees if east is wanted. When the operator looks through the sighting device, he is looking in the desired direction. Conversely when taking the bearing of an object, the operator looks through the sight at the object and can then read its bearing in number of degrees indicated by the weighted end of the needle.

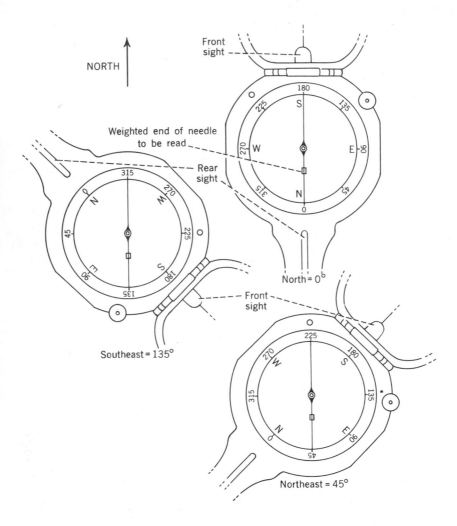

Figure 1. The Brunton-type surveying compass

Three positions are shown. When one looks from the rear sight through the front sight, the direction in which he is looking is indicated by the weighted end of the needle. Note that the unweighted end of the needle always points NORTH and the compass is turned beneath it.

This exercise is designed for the location of a study area by a series of bearings and distances from a permanent object – for example, crossroads, road signs, bench marks (see Figure 2).

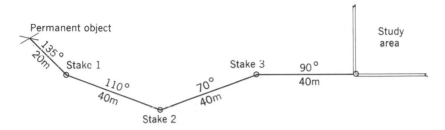

Figure 2. Location of study areas by distance and bearing from permanent objects

The distance between objects is generally measured with a steel tape, but if less accuracy is acceptable, these distances can be paced by students. For this purpose it is useful for each student to measure his normal pace over a standard distance.

Procedure: A. A pair of students set a stake deep enough in the ground so that a tripod with a Brunton-type compass can be placed directly over it. With tripod and compass in place, one member of the pair reads the bearing of the permanent object from this stake. The other records the bearing and meanwhile measures and records the distance between the object and the stake. Bearings and distances may be taken to any other permanent objects available.

     B. One of the pair now becomes the rodman as well as recorder and proceeds in the general direction of the study area with a stadia rod and one end of the measuring tape. The distance and direction should be so chosen that the stadia rod will be visible to the compass man. If convenient, the distance between every two stakes can be kept the same to facilitate later mapping. The compass man calls out the bearing of the rod and the recorder-rodman records bearing and distance and places Stake 2 in place of the stadia rod.

     C. The compass man proceeds to Stake 2, changes jobs with the rodman, and the procedure is repeated until the study area is reached.

Meanwhile other pairs can proceed directly to the study area for Exercise 2.

3

EXERCISE 2. Mapping an area by compasses from the ends of a base line

It is possible to do this exercise with a minimum of three people, but a team of six or seven facilitates the work. These include a leader (or the instructor) who chooses the length and location of the base line and the points, two compass men, a recorder, and two or three rodmen. A practice session on the campus is desirable before field use.

A measured base line with stakes at each end is set out at one side of the area to be mapped and Brunton-type compasses on tripods are placed over the stakes. If any of the points and objects to be placed on the map are not visible from both ends of the base line, a series of base lines is necessary, each new one located from the previous one by bearings and distances (see Exercise 1 and Figure 3).

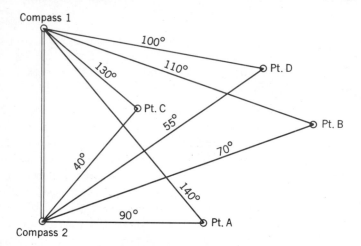

Figure 3. Location of points by compasses from two ends of a base line

Procedure: A. The leader designates the length and bearing of a base line to be set up by the recorder and compass men.

B. When the line is measured, a stake is set at each end, and Brunton-type compasses on tripods are placed over the stakes. Each compass man then reads the bearing of the other compass and adjusts his compass (see directions with the compass) until the bearings are the reciprocal of each other. The recorder records these bearings.

C.   The leader now designates the points and their numbers according to the purpose of the map. Suggestions for points include boundary stakes, paths, roads, rivers, ridges, particular trees, and lower vegetation boundaries.

D.   The rodmen each take a stadia rod and proceed in succession to the indicated points — that is, Rodman 1 goes to Point A, Rodman 2 to Point B, Rodman 1 to Point C, etc.

E.   As soon as the rodman is ready (prearranged arm signals are useful), both compass men read the bearing simultaneously and call it out to the recorder. The second and successive points are taken in order.

F.   Meanwhile the leader makes a sketch map of the area, the base line, the numbered points, and any other features that may aid in a construction of the finished map in the laboratory.

G.   The data and sketch map can be mimeographed and each student can draw a scale map from it with the aid of a ruler and two protractors. It is necessary to use a scale such that the whole area will fit on the chosen paper. First the base line is drawn the proper length and in the proper direction. Then a protractor is placed at each end of the base line to simulate the field position of the compasses. By means of the recorded data from Point A, lines on the correct bearing as indicated on the protractors from each end of the base line are drawn. The intersection of these lines locates Point A, which should be labeled by reference to the Sketch Map. All points can then be located and labeled.

Part Two
Physiognomic Systems

CHAPTER 2 — THE STUDY OF VEGETATION ON A NONFLORISTIC BASIS

In the introduction it was stated that ecologists usually begin with a floristic list of species and proceed from this to determine the role of each species in the vegetation.

It is possible to arrive at a mental picture or a graphic description of the vegetation by a consideration of its physiognomy defined as the general outward appearance of a community. This is determined by the life form of the dominant species without necessarily identifying the species. These nonfloristic systems are particularly valuable to geographers and other nontaxonomists concerned with vegetation. The following exercise will illustrate the concept.

EXERCISE 3. Vegetation on a structural basis

Dansereau (1958) suggests a method by which an image of the vegetation can be provided on a physiognomic basis that does not necessarily require a knowledge of species. Figure 4 indicates the classification used, and Figures 5 and 6 illustrate the method of using symbols in a pictorial representation of the vegetation. The instructor may wish to modify or simplify some of these for class use or the students may be asked to design their own systems with this as a model. On maps the letters designating the vegetation may be used and boundaries of vegetation drawn in. When accompanied by figures similar to Figures 5 and 6, these maps are very descriptive.

As it is not necessary to consider all the categories in a class exercise, the instructor may designate fewer if he desires.

Procedure: A. The whole class should observe the study area first, each student ascertaining the number of life forms present and writing down the various symbols necessary for the vegetation in the area. The instructor should then coordinate these lists, checking to be sure

7

1. LIFE FORM

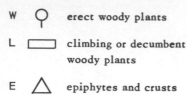

W   erect woody plants

L   climbing or decumbent woody plants

E   epiphytes and crusts

H   herbs

M   bryoids

2. STRATIFICATION

1   more than 25 meters

2   10 — 25 meters

3   8 — 10 meters

4   2 — 8 meters

5   0.5 — 2 meters

6   0.1 — 0.5 meters

7   0.0 — 0.1 meters

3. COVERAGE

b   barren or very sparse

i   interrupted, discontinuous

p   in patches, tufts, clumps

c   continuous

4. FUNCTION

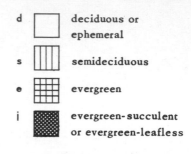

d   deciduous or ephemeral

s   semideciduous

e   evergreen

i   evergreen-succulent or evergreen-leafless

5. LEAF SHAPE AND SIZE

o   leafless

n   needle, spine, scale, or subulate

g   graminoid

a   medium or small

h   broad

v   compound

q   thalloid

6. LEAF TEXTURE

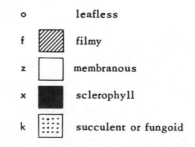

o   leafless

f   filmy

z   membranous

x   sclerophyll

k   succulent or fungoid

Figure 4. The six categories of criteria to be applied to a structural description of vegetation types (Dansereau, 1958)

8

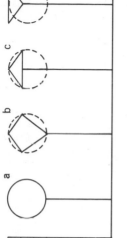

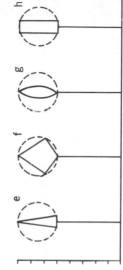

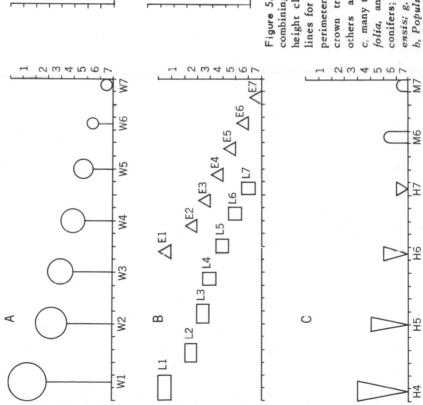

Figure 5. A graphic representation of all the symbols combining criteria 1 (life form) and 2 (stratification or height class) of Figure 4, and a series of crown outlines for tall woody types (W 1, 2, 3), which can fit the perimeter of the symbols in A. *a* is an average globular crown tree, such as *Quercus alba*; examples of the others are as follows: *b, Notholagus cliffortioides; c,* many tropical rainforest trees; *d, Araucaria angusti-folia,* and many palms; *e,* spruces, firs, many other conifers; *f, Pinus ponderosa, P. pinaster, Ilex canari-ensis; g, Juniperus virginiana, Cupressus sempervirens; h, Populus nigra* var. *italica.* (Dansereau, 1958)

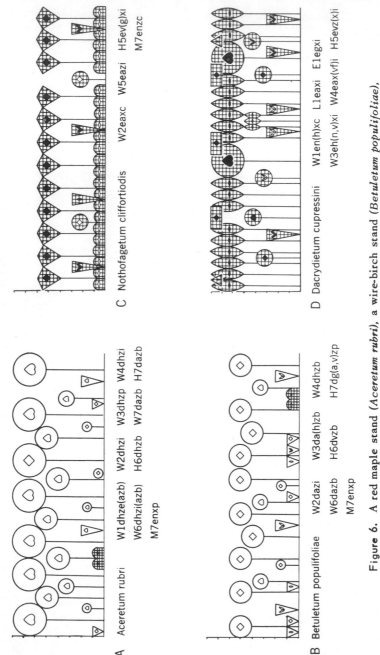

A Aceretum rubri   W1dhze(azb) W2dhzi W3dhzp W4dhzi
                         W6dhzi(azb) H6dhzb W7dazb H7dazb
                         M7enxp

B Betuletum populifoliae W2dazi W3da(h)zb W4dhzb
                           W6dazb H6dvzb   H7dg(a,v)zp
                           M7enxp

C Nothofagetum cliffortiodis W2eaxc W5eazi H5ev(g)xi
                                                M7enzc

D Dacrydietum cupressini W1en(h)xc L1eaxi E1egxi
                           W3eh(n,v)xi W4eax(vf)li H5evz(x)li

Figure 6. A red maple stand (*Aceretum rubri*), a wire-birch stand (*Betuletum populifoliae*),
the beech forest of Arthur's Pass (South Island, New Zealand), and the rimu forest of the
lowlands in the South Island of New Zealand. (Dansereau, 1958).

that all are using the same symbols. The lower vegetation should be considered first to avoid trampling effects.

B. The size of different plants in each life form may be estimated or measured. Tree height may be determined by the use of an Abney Level or Brunton-type compass. Set the compass or the level so that a 45-degree angle is indicated on the right-hand side of the scale. Aim the compass or level at the top of the tree and walk back until the top of the tree and the bubble are visible on the cross-hair at the same time. From this point measure the distance to the tree base. This distance plus the height of one's eye from the ground is the height of the tree. This is derived from a right triangle in which the angle between ground and tree is 90 degrees and the angles between the ground and the line of sight to the top of the tree, and between the line of sight and the tree are both 45 degrees. Thus the two sides of the triangle, the height of the tree and the ground distance, are equal.

C. After the size has been determined, function, leaf shape and size, and leaf texture may be recorded for each life form.

D. Coverage may then be estimated or determined by methods shown in some of the exercises to follow (for example, see Exercise 20). In the lowest level of bryoids, the categories other than size generally will be similar for all species. In the herb layer and above, several different combinations of symbols may be necessary on the basis of differences in height, function, and so forth.

E. On graph paper, prepare a diagram of the vegetation similar to Figure 6 (A, B, C, or D as directed).

F. If the use of species names is desired, a more detailed diagram may be prepared.

EXERCISE 4. The life form system of Raunkiaer

A simpler and more widely used older system of vegetation description on a physiognomic basis is the life form system of Raunkiaer (1934; see also Braun-Blanquet 1932 and Dansereau 1957). Although not so pictorial as Dansereau's system, it has been used by enough ecologists throughout the world to provide interesting comparisons of different vegetational areas. It is based on the position of the highest perennating bud or organ as an indication of the manner in which the plant survives an unfavorable season of cold or dryness. Tables 1 and 2 indicate the symbols, categories, and descriptions used and some sample life form spectra.

Table 1. Raunkiaer's life forms
(Adapted from Raunkiaer, 1934, and Dansereau, 1957)

Symbol	Life Form	Description
Th	Therophyte	Annuals: germination to seeds in one year. Unfavorable season survival as seeds or spores. Widely distributed even in hot, dry deserts.
G	Geophytes	Earth Plants: perennating organs (buds, mycelia) underground and protected. Includes plants with bulbs, tubers, and rhizomes of plants that die above ground.
H	Hemicryptophytes	Perennating bud very close to ground surface. Numerous cryptogams and plants of cold moist regions included, *e.g.*, crustose lichens, thalloid bryophytes, tussock plants, rosettes, scapose plants, many vines and biennials.
Ch	Chamaephytes	Surface Plants: herbaceous or low woody plants with perennating buds above the surface. Carpet mosses, fruticose lichens, creeping herbs, leaf succulents (e.g. *Sedum*), cushion plants, bog mosses, hard grasses (perennials), trailing shrubs, and semishrubs in which upper parts die.
P	Phanerophytes	Aerial Plants: buds high, exposed to weather, with center of distribution in the tropics. Shrubs with buds over 0.5 meter high, trees, stem succulents (cacti), tropical herbs of tree size (Begonia spp.), and lianas.

This exercise can be done in the field or by the use of any floral manual that indicates or implies the desired information.

Procedure in the field:

A. Each student walks throughout the assigned area and determines the life form of each different plant present. It is not necessary to determine the species, but care should be taken that a species is counted but once.

B. The number of different plants in each category is counted and a spectrum similar to Table 2 made for each area.

C. Each spectrum is compared with the world spectrum and the spectra of other given areas and reasons given for differences.

Table 2. Comparative Raunkiaer life form spectra

Region	Th	G	H	Ch	Ph
Normal (Raunkiaer, 1934)	13	6	26	9	46
Swiss Alps (Braun-Blanquet, 1932)	3.5	4	68	24.5	0
Death Valley, California (Braun–Blanquet, 1932)	42	7	18	7	26
Mary's Peak, Oregon (Elevation 4,097 feet) (Merkle, 1951)	0	25	54	2	19
Great Smoky Mountains (Cain, 1945)	3.4	25.8	30.1	4.4	36.3

EXERCISE 5. Profile diagrams of many British ecologists

Profile diagrams for physiognomic descriptions are used by many British ecologists, for example, Richards in Davis and Richards (1933). These diagrams have appeared most often in the British *Journal of Ecology*, but a good example of their use is Beard (1944). Many tables from Dansereau (1957) also illustrate the method. It is possible to use these diagrams as pictorial representations of different vegetation with or without species identifications. Often the diagrams are drawn from strip samples — for example, Loveless and Asprey (1957) — with diagrams from strips 30 meters long and 5 meters wide.

Procedure: A. In the designated area — for example, forest, shrub, or grassland — each pair of students from general observations make preliminary sketches of the general outline-shape and relative size of what appear to be the dominant species in each layer.

B. Next it is necessary to find out the relative coverage of the different plants for the construction of a profile diagram that correctly represents what this vegetation looks like from a side view. This can be estimated or determined by methods shown in some of the exercises to follow (for example, see Exercise 20).

C. Using graph paper to aid in establishing the correct scale, each student constructs a profile-diagram of the dominant vegetation. That plant with the highest cover can be assigned an arbitrary number, for example, four, and thus four individual sketches for that plant would appear in the profile-diagram. Another plant in the same layer with half the cover would be represented by two individual

13

Table 3.   Kuchler's physiognomic classification of vegetation (1949)

CAPITAL LETTERS

Woody Vegetation:
- B : evergreen broadleaf
- D : deciduous broadleaf
- E : evergreen needleleaf (coniferous)
- N : deciduous needleleaf (coniferous)
- O : without leaves

Herbaceous Vegetation:
- G : graminoids
- H : herbs
- L : lichens and mosses

SMALL LETTERS

Group I: *Height:*
- t : tall; minimum height of trees: 25 m
  minimum height of herbaceous plants: 2 m
- m: medium tall; trees: 10–25 m
  herbaceous plants: $\frac{1}{2}$ – 2 m
- l : low; maximum height of trees: 10 m
  maximum height of herbaceous plants: $\frac{1}{2}$ m
- s : shrubs; minimum height: 1 m
- z : dwarf shrubs; maximum height: 1 m

Group II: *Density:*
- c : continuous growth
- i : plants usually do not touch
- p : woody plants scattered singly or in groves
  herbaceous plants in disconnected patches
- r : rare, yet conspicuous
- b : barren; vegetation largely or entirely absent

Group III: *Special Features:*
- e : epiphytes
- j : lianas
- k : succulents
- q : cushion plants
- u : palms
- v : bamboos
- w: aquatic vegetation
- y : tree ferns and tuft plants

14

sketches of that plant. Fractions need to be converted to nearest whole numbers. Approximate heights of the different layers should be indicated on a vertical scale at the left of the diagram.

EXERCISE 6. Küchler's physiognomic system for plant geographers

A modern physiognomic system which uses a series of symbols more flexible than those of previous systems is that of Küchler (1949). A map of the world's vegetation on this basis is designed by Küchler and appears in Goode and Espenshade (1950). Table 3 indicates the symbols and their use.

Each dominant plant in an area is given a series of symbols. Trees, shrubs, and other layers may be separated from each other by placing a period between them in the finished formula. For example a beech-maple forest with some hemlock *(Fagus grandifolia — Acer saccharum* with some *Tsuga canadensis)* might be indicated by:

Dmc. Emi. Dsi. Hlp. Glr. Lir.

Dmc stands for both beech and maple, Emi for hemlock, Dsi for decidu-ous shrubs usually not touching each other, Hlp for low herbs in dis-connected patches, Glr for low graminoids rare yet conspicuous, and Llr for lichens and mosses low and rare yet conspicuous.

Procedure: A. Make general observations and notes regarding the obviously dominant plants in each layer of the designated area.

B. Assign symbols to each dominant plant of each layer by reference to Table 3

C. Design a formula similar to the example. If two plants have the same symbols, it is not necessary to repeat these in the formulas.

D. Compare your formula with any others available and explain the differences. (Students may modify this or design their own systems if the instructor so designates.)

Part Three

Floristic Systems

For more precise analyses, the study of vegetation may also be carried out by a consideration of the species composition. For this purpose, lists of the species to be expected in an area should be prepared by the instructor beforehand. In areas very rich in species, the instructor may include only those that are more prominent or better known. He may even confine the class efforts to shrub and tree species. Certain exercises, however, do require a complete floral list, as will be obvious.

Determination of the role of individual plant species in the vegetation is one of the objectives of plant ecology. What are the more important species, the secondary ones, and the unimportant ones? How are they organized, if at all?

The answer to these questions and others is sought by the analysis of different stands of vegetation and the attempted synthesis of these data from several somewhat similar stands. Should these stands appear sufficiently alike, a community of some rank may be established (see, however, Exercise 46). The chief purpose of data organization is the opportunity to see new relationships, to find answers that cannot be found without this organization.

The analysis of a single stand includes quantitative data of the manner of distribution of species in the stand, of their space requirements, and of their numbers. Qualitative estimates may be made of species' vitality, seasonal variation, and grouping.

The basic principle for all systems of synthesizing data from similar stands is the repeated occurrence of groups of species together. Once a community is established, characteristic or key species may be designated on the basis of their restriction or near restriction to a particular community.

Thus we will be considering frequency, number, area, sociability, vitality, periodicity, stratification, dominance, presence, constancy, and fidelity, among other concepts.

It would be possible to count and measure all of the plants of a stand, but sampling methods have been developed that are as useful and significant and that use less labor and time. The problem is to obtain a sample that properly represents the whole stand. Many of the following exercises involve problems of size, shape, number, and distribution of sample plots.

Generally the class data should be mimeographed for distribution and a master file kept. Many of the exercises use data from other exercises. Adding machines, calculators, and slide rules are desirable for data handling.

CHAPTER 3 —— FREQUENCY

In the Scandinavian countries where vegetation is comparatively sparse in cover and species, the emphasis has been on frequency determination for vegetational analysis. Frequency expresses the percentage of sample plots in which a given species occurs. If sample plots are distributed throughout an area to be investigated and the number of plots in which each species occurs is recorded, an estimate is obtained of the distribution of these species, one of the quantities important in determining the comparative role of species in the vegetation.

EXERCISE 7. **Stick and radius rod method (Raunklaer, 1934)**.

The stick and radius rod method is applicable to low and medium vegetation, but if modified by the use of a center pole and measuring tape and the plot area enlarged to 10 square meters, this method can be used in forests.

For low vegetation the area of each sample plot is suggested as 0.1 square meter and for medium vegetation 1.0 square meter. Instead of a stick and radius rod, it is simpler to use a brightly colored stick to which is attached a string of the correct radius. After the stick is thrown, it is stuck into the ground where it lands, and the string is rotated to mark the circumference of the sample plot.

In forest use it is better to use a stick 2 meters long with four heavy strings attached, since it is difficult to rotate a single string in this kind of vegetation.

Procedure: A. In the designated area, toss the stick and radius string the designated number of times (if time permits, a minimum of 100 per class).

B. Check the occurrence of each species on the provided species list which should be alphabetically arranged with species at the left followed by a series of columns, one for each toss. For this exercise it is not necessary to count the individuals at each toss but merely to put a check in the column representing that toss.

C. In the last column of the species list, which should be headed "Frequency," record the frequency percent of each species. This percent is obtained by dividing the number of plots in which the species occurred by the total number of plots and multiplying by 100.

D. Make a table in which the species of higher frequencies are at the top.

EXERCISE 8. Effects of the number of samples

Procedure: A. Using the data from Exercise 7 by groups of ten sample plots each, plot points on a graph similar to Figure 7.

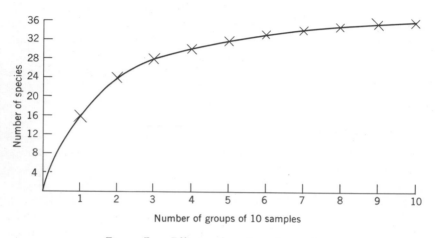

Figure 7. Effects of number of samples

For the first group of ten, plot the total number of species occurring. For each successive point, add those species that are new to a cumulative total. For example, if for the first group of ten, sixteen species were present, then the plotted point would be as in the sample above. If in the next group of ten, there are eight additional species not previously found, then the next plotted point would be at twenty-four regardless of the total number of species in the second group. The third group might have four additional species, and so on.

From this plot can be determined how many plots are necessary to sample the vegetation adequately. Cain (1938) states that sampling is adequate when a 10 percent increase in sample area results in an increase of species equaling 10 percent of the total present. If, for instance, referring to Figure 7, the total number of species in this vegetation area was thirty-six, 10 percent would be 3.6 species. The point at which a percent increase in area results in this much increase in number of species is somewhere between two and four groups of ten samples, since there is an increase of four species from two to

20

three and increase of two species between three and four. By this system, four groups of ten samples each would be adequate.

Braun-Blanquet (1932) considers the sample adequate when the curve becomes horizontal. In Figure 7 this point is between five and seven.

Once the number of samples necessary for an adequate sample has been determined for one kind of vegetation, other stands of similar vegetation can be sampled more efficiently by fewer sample plots.

B. Does your graph indicate an adequate number of sample plots for your area? If so, what is the number according to Cain's (1938) suggestion? According to Braun-Blanquet (1932)?

EXERCISE 9. Effect of size of sampling units

Procedure: A. Over the same area used in Exercise 7 take the same number of samples with stick and radius strings of twice the size. Record frequencies by groups of ten samples as before. Compare resultant frequencies of two (or more) of the most frequent species resulting from the same number of different sized sample plots. Then compare the results of equal total areas — that is, the total number of smaller-sized plots with one-half that number of larger plots.

B. Repeat Exercise 8 for the data received from the double-sized plots.

C. Compare the number of sample plots necessary for the two different sizes.

Exercise 9 may be repeated with half-size plots. In large classes different groups may be assigned different-sized plots the same day.

EXERCISE 10. Effect of the shape of sampling units

Procedure: In the same area (or in areas for which good data are available from other years for comparison), take the same number of sample plots by means of a square frame 1 square meter in area and record the frequency of species. (Note: Time may be saved, if desired, by considering the most frequent species only.) Compare the frequencies obtained by the circles and the squares. Do you think the shape that gives the higher frequencies is more adequate? Why?

This exercise may be repeated with any desired shape of sample plot. For instance, recent studies have indicated the advantage of rectangular plots in some vegetation (Bormann, 1953).

Considering all the species present, make a graph similar to that in Exercise 8 to compare the number of square sample plots with the number of round ones that are necessary for adequate sampling.

EXERCISE 11. Effect of distribution of samples

A fuller consideration of this problem is found in Part VII, but at this point it is possible to evaluate to some extent the effects of sample distribution. Samples may be distributed at random with every part of the area having an equal chance of being sampled, or they may be distributed systematically, widely and evenly throughout the area. The advantage of random sampling is the possibility of statistical treatment to assess amount of error. On the other hand, systematic sampling may be more likely to include variations within a stand. Tossing of a stick is not truly random since the distance it can be tossed is limited, and the place of beginning is chosen somewhat subjectively.

The best method of random distribution is to grid the area and select numbers from a random numbers table, for instance, in Snedecor (1956). A rough chart of the area is drawn to scale, and a series of intersecting horizontal and vertical lines drawn to make squares of the desired sample size (Figure 8).

The size of the area and the desired size of the sample plots will determine the number of divisions on the grid and the number of co-ordinates necessary to locate a sample plot. As an example, in a large area, a grid 1000 meters long by 1000 meters wide may be established. In the field it is best to use strong rope for the boundaries and lighter rope every 10 meters in both directions to facilitate the location of sample plots. Since the lines are 1000 meters long, at least three digits, ranging from 000 to 999, are needed to locate a point on the horizontal and the vertical axis. The 1000 squares are numbered along the top and down the sides as illustrated. In smaller areas 100 squares or any other number can be chosen. With 100, only four digits would be necessary, for coordinates from 00 to 99 on each axis. If a rectangular area is sampled, the long axis can be divided into 1000 parts and the short axis into a smaller number. Some of the sets of digits from a random numbers table will give coordinates that are too large to be used on this shorter axis and these sets are skipped.

Systematic sampling is done by distributing the sample plots evenly along compass lines. This exercise is better as a class project.

Procedure: A. One group make a grid on graph paper of the designated area to scale as described above, and then set ropes and stakes in the field.

       B. Meanwhile another group using a random numbers table (or, alternatively drawing numbered beans from a bag) select the

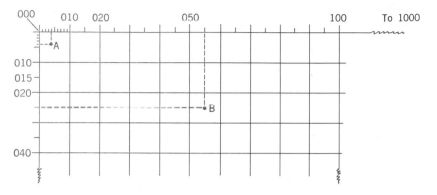

Figure 8.   Method of numbering grids
Coordinates of "A" = 004, 004 and of
"B" = 055, 025

numbered plots to be sampled. The procedure is to flip open the table
to any chance page and place a pencil aimlessly on some digit. This
digit and the subsequent three digits are used to fix the point of the
first sample. As an example, the digits 4312 would mean the forty-
third row and the twelfth column of the table, and thus indicate the
first digit of the coordinates of sample one. In Snedecor's (1956)
ten thousand randomly assorted digits table 1.5.1, the digit thus indicated is "six". The number of sample plots to be taken is decided
next (for instance, 100). One hundred groups of six numbers each
would be selected by proceeding from that digit "six" in any direction
consecutively. In each group of six numbers, the first three give the
horizontal coordinate and the last three the vertical coordinate of
each sample in turn.

   C.   In the field, the random numbers indicating the location of each sample may be divided between members of the class.
Each student then locates his sample plots and obtains frequency
figures for the designated species, see Exercise 7. As an example of
the location of a plot, suppose six figures to be 055025. Assume the
field scale is such that the whole area is 1000 meters square, therefore gridded by a series of ropes into 10-meter squares. Proceed along
the horizontal axis past the fifth light rope (050) and then measure 5
meters more to reach 055. Then proceed down the vertical axis 5
meters beyond the second rope and the intersection is the location of
the sample plot corner (see Figure 8, point B). This corner, for instance, the northwest corner, should be the same for all plots.

D. The assigned group for the area uses graph paper to plan the location of 100 sample plots, systematically and evenly spaced with 10 rows of 10 plots each.

E. In the field these plots should be divided evenly among the various groups. Each group locate the assigned sample plot and record the frequency of the same species for which frequencies were obtained in the randomly distributed plots. Total the class data.

F. Each student compare these two methods with each other and with complete census data if available. Which one gives the greater number of species? Is this significant? Explain.

CHAPTER 4 — ABUNDANCE AND DENSITY

Obviously in a consideration of the relative importance of species in a population, the numbers or abundance of the individual species should be considered. Often this is estimated, but for more precise work, actual counting is more valuable, leading to a quantity called "density," the average number of individuals per sampled area, or per unit area.

The regular practice is to use somewhat larger sample plots than those used for frequency determinations, so that the recommended sizes are as follows: for low vegetation, 1 square meter; for medium vegetation, 4 square meters, and for higher vegetation (trees), 10 square meters. Since larger plots are used, it is customary to take fewer plots. It should be emphasized that in elementary class work as many plots should be taken as time permits.

EXERCISE 12. Abundance

Procedure: A. Each pair take five sample plots of the recommended size, scattered by tosses of the stick and radius string or square frame as directed. Opposite the species list, in separate columns for each sample plot, record the number of stems of each species in each sample plot. (It should generally be decided beforehand by instructor and students what constitutes a countable stem when dealing with some plants, in clumps of grass or shrubs, so that results of all teams are comparable.)

B. Express the results in a table with the most abundant species at the top.

C. Compare the relative rank of species in this list with the rank of species in frequency tables or any other list available from this same study area.

D. Previous exercises on size, shape and number of sample plots can be repeated to determine their influence on abundance.

EXERCISE 13. Density

Procedure: A. Using the data from Exercise 12 express the results as density — that is, the number of individuals of each species per square meter. This is done by adding the total number of each species for the total sample area and dividing by the total sample area in square meters.

B. Using frequency figures from the same area (Exercise 7) and from a sample of comparable size, can you discover a relationship between frequency and density? Then look up Blackman (1935).

EXERCISE 14. Tree counts for abundance

Since the establishment of sample plots in forests is more difficult than in lower vegetation, certain other methods have been devised to obtain records of abundance and some other quantities. One previous difficulty in sampling with classes has been the tendency, even when compasses are used, for various groups to cross each other's paths. This can be obviated by having the group walk to the center of the plot as the instructor points out and identifies trees as necessary. Once in the center pairs can be sent out along radii.

Procedure: A. Each pair move from the center toward the outer edge of the area and record on the species list the number of each species encountered until a total of 100 (or any number time permits) is reached. The width of the band to be considered is customarily two meters, the tally-man holding a meter stick out to either side of himself, and counting tree trunks hit by the sticks, folding sticks back when necessary to pass between trees. It is helpful if the recorder keeps a separate cumulative record of total trees so that he knows when 100 has been reached. Instead of the first 100 trees, a belt of a definite length and width — for example, 100 meters long by 2 meters wide — may be chosen.

B. Express the results in a table as percentage abundance by dividing the total number of trees of each species by the total number of all trees and multiplying by 100. Place the most abundant species at the top of the list.

C. If figures for density are desired, the distance necessary to obtain 100 trees can be paced off by the recorder as he records, and this distance multiplied by the 2-meter width will give an estimate of the area covered by each pair. If more accuracy is desired, the area can be measured by a tape.

D. Compare the data obtained by this method with other data available for this area. Do you think your samples were adequate? Explain.

EXERCISE 15. Estimates in degrees of abundance as used in Great Britain (Tansley and Adamson, 1913)

Many ecologists in Great Britain prefer to estimate abundance with the use of scales, designating classes by letters or numbers. Although the value of this method is to some extent dependent upon experience and training for reproducible results, the use of scales of estimate often gives the necessary information in less time and in situations where counting merely substantiates the obvious. One scale is as follows:

d = dominant
va = very abundant
a = abundant
f = frequent
o = occasional
r = rare
vr = very rare

Sometimes a species occurs in great numbers in a very small part of the general area, so that it is useful to use the letter "l" in front of any of the letters above to indicate "local" abundance.

Procedure: A. Walk through the area with the provided species list and mark the appropriate symbol from the above list after each species present.

B. Make a table in which the species are listed in order of abundance.

C. If this area has been sampled by other methods of determining abundance, compare the results and make conclusions. Part of the class could use this method while the others are using different methods.

EXERCISE 16.   Abundance related to distance between plants

It has long been realized that the distance between individuals is a measure of their abundance and a recent scale has been established to relate them. Acocks (1953) has set up the following:

vvab	extremely abundant	1 in. apart
vab	very abundant	3 in. apart
ab +		4.5 in. apart
ab	abundant	6 in. apart
ab −		9 in. apart
c +		1 ft apart
c	common	1.25 ft apart
c −		1.6 ft apart
f +		2 ft. apart
f	frequent	3 ft apart
f −		6 ft apart

ff +		12 ft apart
ff	fairly frequent	15 ft apart
ff −		20 ft apart
o +		30 ft apart
o	occasional	50 ft apart
r +		125 ft apart
r	rare	200 ft apart
vr	very rare	300 ft apart (and over)

The letter "l" can be used in front of any of the letters above to indicate local abundance, for instance, "lab" or "lc", (see Exercise 15). This scale may be modified to include fewer categories.

Procedure: A. Each pair begin with the more abundant species from the provided list and make a series of measurements between individuals of the same species. It is not possible to indicate the number of measurements necessary but a general guide is that the more closely successive measurements agree, the fewer measurements are necessary and vice versa.

B. Average these measurements, consult the scale above, and place the correct letter symbol after each species considered.

C. If other data are available, compare this method with other methods for obtaining abundance and make conclusions. Compare your estimates with those of other members of the class.

CHAPTER 5 — COVER AND BASAL AREA

Frequency indicates the distribution of species, whereas abundance and density indicate numbers. In an area where trees and grass occur together, abundance and to some extent frequency might indicate grasses as more important than the less numerous though overtowering trees. Thus another analytic quantity, that of area, needs consideration. Cover is the term generally used to indicate the area occupied by species, and is usually a measure of area covered by the crown, the stem, or a patch if the vegetation occurs in this pattern. For trees the crown is probably a better measure, but the stem is often more convenient to measure. Many ecologists use cover or basal area for the recognition of the dominant species.

EXERCISE 17. Cover degrees by guided estimate

The instructor may choose to consider any number or type of species in this exercise or even consider larger groupings, for example, shrubs versus grasses versus herbs versus mosses versus lichens, etc. Fewer numbers and larger plots may also be used in this exercise; in larger classes, a series of small and large plots may be compared.

Since it is time-consuming to measure the actual vertical projection downward to the ground of the plant crown, a common practice is to use a scale for guided estimates. This scale is usable for sample plots up to 10 square meters in vegetation that is rather homogeneous. The size of sample plot should be similar to those prescribed for different types of vegetation in Exercise 7. A useful scale is that of Trepp (1950), which combines cover and abundance and gives an average percentage cover which allows the combining of figures from several samples to obtain an average for all samples taken.

Scale	Percent range of cover	Average percent of cover
x	to 1.0	0.1
1	1 — 9.9	5.0
2	10 — 24.9	17.5
3	25 — 49.9	37.5
4	50 — 74.9	62.5
5	75 — 100.0	87.5

Procedure: A. Each student toss the stick and radius string or the square frame ten times, and for each sample estimate the average percent of cover according to the above scale. Record this number opposite each species in the species list. One hundred samples should be taken per class, if time permits.

B. Total the average percentage cover for each species for all samples taken by the class and divide each by the total number of samples to obtain an average percentage. Convert this to a single scale number for each species and make a list of species in order of cover scales with the highest at the top. Compare this method with others used.

EXERCISE 18. Cover by stem diameter — trees

Meter sticks can be marked off to give direct readings of the area covered by tree trunks at 4.5 feet from the ground (breast height, the height at which diameters are taken in American forestry), and these figures give a good estimate of the relative importance of trees on a cover basis. Alternatively, the diameters can be recorded and averaged first and then converted to basal area by reference to Table 4. Instead of recording the actual diameter of each tree, it is faster and more convenient to group the trees into diameter classes. Up to five classes should be selected, in such a way that each class has the same range. For example, if the larger trees have a diameter of 35 centimeters and the smallest ones to be considered have a diameter of 10 centimeters, then the classes should be 35 minus 10 divided by 5, or 5 centimeters apart, as follows:

Classes

1	10 — 15 cm diameter at breast height
2	15 — 20 cm diameter at breast height
3	20 — 25 cm diameter at breast height
4	25 — 30 cm diameter at breast height
5	30 — 35 cm diameter at breast height

An alphabetical list of the tree species with headings of the diameter classes in separate vertical columns should be prepared beforehand. Five additional columns at the right-hand side should be prepared for the recording of total basal area of each diameter class for each species.

Often basal area readings for individual trees are taken directly from the tables. Aids to accurate diameter determination are diameter tapes, marked so that the diameter can be read by encircling the tree with the tape – that is, the circumference is converted on the tape to diameter.

Procedure: A. Each pair proceed as in Exercise 14 either with the first 100 trees, or in a belt 100 meters by 2 meters, but record the individuals of each species as they are encountered under the appropriate diameter classes.

B. The number of trees that occur in each diameter class for each species should then be multiplied by a factor from Table 4 which is entered with the mean diameter of each class. As an example, for the 25– to 30–centimeter class, the average is 27.5 centimeters which gives a basal area from the table of 593.9 square centimeters; therefore the number of trees of a species in this diameter class is multiplied by 593.9 to obtain the basal area. Put the basal areas in the correct columns.

Table 4. Diameter (cm or in.) to basal area (sq cm or sq in.)
(Other figures necessary may be obtained from any edition of the "Handbook of Physics and Chemistry," in the numerical tables for reciprocals, circumference, and area of circles.)

1.0– 0.78	11.0– 95.03	21.0–346.4	31.0– 754.8	41.0–1320
1.5– 1.77	11.5–103.9	21.5–363.1	31.5– 779.3	41.5–1353
2.0– 3.14	12.0–113.1	22.0–380.1	32.0– 804.2	42.0–1385
2.5– 4.91	12.5–122.7	22.5–397.6	32.5– 829.6	42.5–1419
3.0– 7.07	13.0–132.7	23.0–415.5	33.0– 855.3	43.0–1452
3.5– 9.62	13.5–143.1	23.5–433.7	33.5– 881.4	43.5–1486
4.0–12.57	14.0–153.9	24.0–452.4	34.0– 907.9	44.0–1521
4.5–15.91	14.5–165.1	24.5–471.4	34.5– 934.8	44.5–1555
5.0–19.63	15.0–176.7	25.0–490.9	35.0– 962.1	45.0–1590
5.5–23.76	15.5–188.7	25.5–510.7	35.5– 989.8	45.5–1626
6.0–28.27	16.0–201.1	26.0–530.9	36.0–1018	46.0–1661
6.5–33.18	16.5–213.8	26.5–551.5	36.5–1046	46.5–1698
7.0–38.48	17.0–227.0	27.0–527.5	37.0–1075	47.0–1735
7.5–44.18	17.5–240.5	27.5–593.9	37.5–1104	47.5–1772
8.0–50.27	18.0–254.5	28.0–615.7	38.0–1134	48.0–1809
8.5–56.75	18.5–268.8	28.5–637.9	38.5–1164	48.5–1847
9.0–63.62	19.0–283.5	29.0–660.5	39.0–1195	49.0–1886
9.5–70.88	19.5–298.6	29.5–683.5	39.5–1225	49.5–1924
10.0–78.54	20.0–314.2	30.0–706.9	40.0–1257	50.0–1963
10.5–86.59	20.5–330.1	30.5–730.6	40.5–1288	50.5–2003

C. If it is desired and time permits and the length of the area is measured, the results may be expressed in basal area per unit area.

D. Compare these results to those obtained by other methods in this area.

EXERCISE 19. Cover by stem diameter for grasses, herbs, or shrubs

With the use of small calipers, Exercise 18 can be adapted for use with smaller plants. If the same area as that for Exercise 13 is used, the number of individuals of different species per square meter has already been obtained. Otherwise this should be obtained in addition to the following.

Procedure: A. Each pair select 100 stems of each of the assigned species (all or part at the instructor's discretion), and measure their diameters.

B. Add class data for diameters of each species and divide by the total number of stems to get an average diameter for each species.

C. Using data from Exercise 13 or new data collected similarly, multiply the number of individuals per square meter of each species by its average area to obtain the cover of each species per square meter.

D. Make a list of species and their cover in order with the highest at the top.

E. Vegetation changes can be followed by use of this method in successive years. If data are available from other years for this area, compare your results with them.

EXERCISE 20. The line-intercept method of determining cover (Canfield, 1941)[*]

The line-intercept method is useful for the determination of cover by a consideration of the total length of each species along a line in comparison with the total length of the line. Different levels of vegetation are usually sampled separately, the lower vegetation first to obtain data before disturbance. As many categories as desired may be sampled — for instance, moss-lichen, herb, grass, shrub, and tree levels. For convenience in measuring and in order to insure the in-

---

[*] See Buell and Cantlon (1950) for a good example of its use and for an ingenious cover sight device.

clusion of smaller species, it is desirable to consider all the vegetation intercepted by a strip 1 centimeter wide on one side of the line.

With the aid of a centimeter rule, linear measurements of the extent along the line of each species in the different layers of vegetation is made. Grasses, grass-like plants, rosette-forming plants, herbs, and weeds are measured at the ground surface. Shrubs, half-shrubs, and trees are measured by the crown-spread intercept — that is, the downward extension of the crown onto the line.

As one proceeds from the beginning of the line, data is recorded as in a transect (see Exercise 25) in order of occurrence of the species. Thus the data might look as follows:

Layer 1.   Al (symbol for a particular plant species) 1.2 cm, Ca 3.1 cm, Av 6.2 cm, etc.

Layer 2.   Ct 14 cm, Hg 21 cm, etc.

For some studies the stems of the upper layers are measured for their extent along the line in lower layers. The class should decide this before the exercise to insure uniform treatment.

Procedure: A.   Each pair lay out a line 20 meters long located by the toss of a stick.   In sparse vegetation, for instance some deserts, where the vegetation cover is less than 3 percent of the ground surface, the length of the line should be doubled.

B.   Beginning with the lower layers, record the length along the line of each of the species in order as encountered.

C.   Now each pair lay out additional lines, if time permits, to make a total of 16 for the class.   (This is generally considered to be the minimum number for the adequate sampling of a stand.)

D.   Make a list of species, separated according to levels, with those species of highest cover at the top.   Compare this list with other lists for this area.

E.   Count each separate occurrence of a species along the line.   For each species divide its number of occurrences by the total occurrences of all species.   What quantity previously studied does this figure represent?   Percent cover by species can also be calculated from this data and can then be compared with basal area as a measure of dominance.

EXERCISE 21.   Cover by the point-observation method

The point-observation method was a standard grassland analysis procedure in the United States for a number of years.   Circular plots are most commonly used, and cover for each category or species of plant estimated with or without the use of aiding devices, for instance, plastic squares. In grass or other comparatively low vegetation, sticks and radius strings or square frames can be used. In higher vegetation, stakes or poles and tapes circumscribing larger plots are used, and larger devices can be constructed to aid in cover estimation. This is not truly a *point* method (see Chapter 7) but gets its name from the center pin originally used.

Procedure: A.   Each pair set out ten sample plots by the use of a 1-square-meter frame.

B.   Estimate the cover percentage of each species (or category of plants if directed) by placing the 1-square-decimeter plastic square over the plants and counting the number of times the square covers a given species (or category). Fractions of squares may be indicated and added. Since the plastic square goes into the sample plot 100 times, the number of squares (or fractions) necessary to cover a given species is the cover percentage for that species. The instructor may designate certain prominent species to be considered or may divide the vegetation into categories, for instance, tall grass, short grass, herbs, and shrubs.

C.   Make a list of species (or categories) in order of cover percentage with the species of highest cover at the top.

D.   Does this method give comparable results to other methods? Compare your data with class averages. Determine how many plots are necessary for an adequate sample (see Exercise 8).

EXERCISE 22.   Cover by the Braun-Blanquet combined scale

Many different scales of estimate have been used for the determination of cover degree. One of the most widely used in Europe is the combined cover-abundance scale of Braun-Blanquet (1932):

    x = sparsely or very sparsely present, cover very small
    1 = plentiful but of small cover value
    2 = very numerous, or covering at least 1/20 of the area
    3 = any number of individuals covering 1/4 to 1/2 the area
    4 = any number of individuals covering 1/2 to 3/4 the area
    5 = covering more than 3/4 of the area

Thus the smaller numbers are concerned with abundance and the higher ones with cover.

In practice, Braun-Blanquet first makes a survey of a homogeneous vegetation recording all of the species present. Then he selects a small sample plot in a representative place within the uniform area. Within the small sample plot, he assigns one figure from the combined cover-abundance scale and another figure for sociability (see Exercise 37). If in this small plot he does not record all or most of the species on his list, he continues to enlarge the sample plot until practically all of the species are encountered. The size of the sample necessary to include most of the species in homogeneous vegetation is one of the characteristics which can distinguish one vegetation from another and will vary for different types. This point is reached when the plotted curve of area and number of species becomes approximately horizontal.

Procedure: A. Each pair of students set out a one-square-meter plot with the square frame (larger in higher vegetation as in previous exercises) and record opposite each species of the list an estimate from the combined cover-abundance scale and another figure, separated by a period from the first, for sociability from the sociability scale (see Exercise 37). The initial size of the plot will depend upon the vegetation and should be large enough to include at least the obvious dominants. As examples, in a prairie stand that includes five dominant grass species among others, the initial quadrat should probably be large enough to include these, whereas in a coniferous forest, a larger plot would be necessary to include the different trees dominant in the tree layer.

B. If a significant number of species is absent, double the plot size and proceed as before with the new species. The amount of increase in size of the sample plot is a matter of judgment because of the variation in vegetation. In general, the greater the number of species missing, the greater the increase in size should be. If a very few species are missing, then the enlargement increments should be smaller.

C. Continue to enlarge the sample plot until most of the species on your list occur. This is also a matter of judgment, for in a vegetation with some rare species, it might be possible to take the whole area as a sample plot before encountering some of these species. For elementary work, the instructor may restrict his list somewhat in the light of this.

D. Make a list of species in order of cover-abundance with the highest ones on top, and record the area of your sample. Compare your results with others in the class.

EXERCISE 23. Determination of cover by charting

In some detailed investigations, the time and effort required for making an actual representation of the vegetation on a chart may be justified. This is true of successive studies with permanent sample plots (see Exercises 32–34). Graph paper is most generally used for the chart and a scale is established so that the field plot to be charted will fit on the paper. The plot itself is usually set out by ropes and then subdivided by strings so that the plot squares correspond to squares on graph paper. Naturally this method is of most use in low vegetation, but it can be adapted for forest use, by charting trees with compasses and base lines (see Exercise 2). Often a ruler or tape is of advantage in measuring the area covered by the plants. Plastic squares, as used in Exercise 21, may also be helpful.

When grasslands are being studied, the basal area is drawn for each plant occupying more than 0.5 square centimeter. Plants occupying less area are indicated by dots. Standard symbols similar to those used by the forest or range experiment stations in your area may be used on the chart to indicate the species. For instance, use the first letter of the genus and species plus other letters when necessary to avoid confusion: *Poa pratensis* = Pp. It is recommended that for elementary classes the use of this method be illustrated on low grasses, mosses, or lichens (see Exercise 33).

Procedure: A. Each pair set out four stakes enclosing an area of 1 square meter (or for mosses and lichens 1 square decimeter). Pass a strong rope around the stakes and attach it; then tie nine strings between each pair of opposite ropes. It is possible to construct a permanent light metal frame with strings attached, and with bolts, and wing nuts on the corners. (This can be folded for storage.) This will mark a grid in which each subdivision is ten square centimeters. Obtain graph paper which contains subdivisions of one square centimeter and, using the scale of 10:1, plot the vegetation present.

       B. For each species count the squares and fractions of squares covered, sllowing 0.5 square centimeter for dots and record totals. This figure gives the percentage of the total area of the quadrat covered by a species. For example, if a species covers three squares out of the 100 total, it covers 3 percent of the plot area.

       C. List the species in order of cover and compare this list with lists obtained in this study area by other methods of cover determination. If this area has been charted previously, compare your chart with previous ones.

EXERCISE 24. Determination of cover by charting with a pantograph

Instead of measuring the area covered by the vegetation, it is possible to use a pantograph to aid in the charting of vegetation. This is a device that is used to change the scale of a drawing. It can be set so that when the tracing arm is moved to encircle the vegetation, the recording arm records the outline on graph paper on a reduced scale. Various modifications have been made to facilitate its use in the field, but for elementary class use it is suggested that an ordinary one be used to chart moss or lichen vegetation on soil or rocks. Since normally only one pantograph per class is justifiable, other pairs of students can do other exercises while one pair uses the pantograph.

Procedure: A. Each pair choose a patch of moss or lichen that is on a fairly even surface and set up the pantograph on a scale of one to five. Choose a size of plot that will fit on the available graph paper. One member guide the tracing pen around the moss or lichen boundaries and the other the recording arm on the graph paper. If desired appropriate symbols may be placed on the graph paper to indicate species. Permanent stakes may be set for relocation.

B. Count the squares and fractions that each species or different type of plant covers on the graph paper and express the relative coverage for each by dividing the area covered by the total area drawn.

C. Compare this method with other methods of obtaining cover in the given area.

CHAPTER 6 — TRANSECTS

A transect is an elongated sample plot in which the vegetational data are recorded in order as species are encountered in the plot. It is useful to indicate transitions in vegetation, as between associations or, for instance, on slopes containing different zones of vegetation. Recent studies have indicated that its use within some associations gives better data than does the use of square plots, perhaps because it may more closely resemble the dissemination pattern of vegetation. Thus many of the preceding exercises can be performed with the use of transects instead of the previously recommended shapes. If one considers a transect as a series of contiguous plots with the data recorded in segments, frequency can also be calculated.

EXERCISE 25. Use of a transect to determine vegetational transitions

Procedure: A. Each pair set up two lines 1 meter apart and 10 meters long in an area in which a change in the vegetation is apparent from one end of the line to the other. The length of the line is determined by the kind of vegetation, as in previous exercises.

B. In a left-hand column in your notebook indicate the successive meters, 0-1, 1-2, 2-3, and so forth.

C. Placing a meter stick across the ropes 1 meter from one end, list all the plants occurring in the 0-1 meter section.

D. Next place another meter stick at the 2-meter mark and record all the plants in the 1-2 meter section. Continue meter by meter to the end of the line.

E. Present your data in the form of a graph. Correlate the change in vegetation with some factor of the environment if possible. For instance, if it is elevation along a slope, distance from a stream, or an obviously different soil type, indicate this on your graph.

F. If so directed, make another graph of the data from odd numbered segments, 1, 3, 5, 7, and so on. Compare this with the previous graph. Do this also for the even-numbered plots, and compare with data from all the plots and from the odd-numbered plots. Are the samples adequate when plots are skipped no longer than the transect is wide?

CHAPTER 7 — PLOTLESS METHODS

As so much time is necessary for setting out plots, methods have been developed recently for more rapid sampling without plots. Generally a larger number of samples are necessary, but they are more quickly taken. The following exercises illustrate the methods.

EXERCISE 26. Point-frame method (Levy and Madden, 1933)

A framework containing pins (Figure 9) is used to sample vegetation lower than the frame. As the pins are pushed through the holes to the ground, each plant species hit is counted. This method has been used most widely in grass lands but can be used in other types of low vegetation as well. The most satisfactory recording of results seems to be the number of hits for each species per 100 points taken.

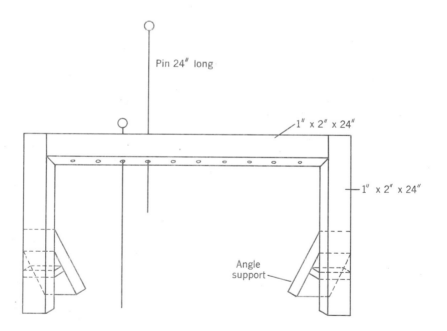

Pin 24″ long

1″ x 2″ x 24″

1″ x 2″ x 24″

Angle support

Figure 9. The point-frame
This can be constructed for use vertically or at an angle, as shown.

Procedure: A. Each pair set up the point-frame ten different times. At each sampling place, push each of the ten pins in turn through the hole until it touches the ground. Record opposite each species in your list the number of hits from 100 pins. Count only those species actually touched by the pin.

    B. Make a list of species with those with the highest number of hits per 100 at the top.

    C. To what quantity previously discussed is this number most comparable?

    D. Compare this method with others used.

EXERCISE 27. Bitterlich method, or the plotless sampling for trees (Grosenbaugh, 1952)

    This variable-radius plotless method is based on the principle of point-sampling. A hand-held anglegauge consisting of a stick 33 inches long by about 2 inches wide is fitted at both ends with rectangular pieces of tin extending vertically on the upper side of the stick. Each piece of tin is exactly one inch wide, and one has a peep-hole drilled in it. Two lines from the edges of the other piece of tin intersecting at the peep-hole form an angle there of 104.18 minutes. This angle is so chosen that when the number of trees is divided by the number of points taken and the quotient is multiplied by ten, the resultant figure is the basal area in square feet per acre. Prism-angle gauges are now on the market which can be used in place of the stick.

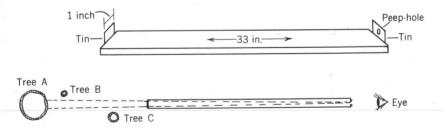

Figure 10.   Bitterlich stick

Trees A and C would be counted since they are larger than the angle. Thus the tallying of a tree is a function of size and distance away.

In use a series of points is set up along a compass line. At each point, the Bitterlich stick is pointed at all trees as one rotates himself at the point. All trees are counted that appear *larger* than the piece of tin at the end opposite the peep-hole — that is, that subtend an angle greater than that of the Bitterlich stick. The species of the trees are also recorded.

Procedure: A. Each pair, starting from the center of the forest and working out along a radius, take a series of ten points, sufficiently far apart so that successive points do not sample the same trees.

        B. At each point, count the number of trees of each species that appear larger than the stick end piece. (*Note:* The species of tree is not important if a consideration of total yield alone is desired.)

        C. Figure and record for each tree species the following: basal area in square feet per acre; percentage composition (by dividing the number of trees of each species by the total number of trees of all species and multiplying by 100); and the percentage species frequency (by considering each point as a sample plot, and for each species dividing the number of points of its occurrence by the total number of points and multiplying by 100).

        D. Compare the data from this method with any other data available for the same. For instance, the same area may be sampled by methods of Exercises 18, 20, 28, or 29.

Random pairs and quarter methods (Cottam and Curtis, 1949, 1955, 1956)

The random pairs and the quarter methods are examples of several new methods developed since 1947 to utilize spacing distances instead of fixed-area sample plots. Rather than sampling a small area in terms of abundance, the amount of area occupied by each plant is ascertained. This amount of area called 'mean area," is the reciprocal of the density. When used for forests, only trees over 10 centimeters (4 inches) in diameter are considered.

The differences in these methods consist largely in the manner in which individual plants are chosen so that measurements between them give an accurate determination of the mean area and density. Although these methods were developed for forest studies, they have been used by Pomona College students in California desert studies of creosote bush *(Larrea divaricata)*, cacti, and also some discontinuous shrub types.

EXERCISE 28.   Random pairs method

In the random pairs method trees are chosen by means of an exclusion angle.   Different angles have been used but at present one of 180 degrees is recommended as best.

A predetermined compass line pattern, zigzag or straight, is set up for the study area, and the distance of the points from each other is chosen so that successive points sample different trees.   Figure 11 illustrates the method.   From the first point the nearest tree, "A", is chosen and its diameter and species recorded.

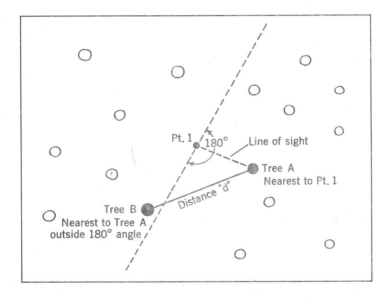

Figure 11.   Random pairs method
The species and diameter of Tree A, the nearest tree to the point, are recorded.   The 180-degree sector including Tree A is excluded from consideration for the choice of the second member of the pair. Rather, Tree B is selected since it is the nearest tree to Tree A that is outside the 180-degree sector.   The species and diameter of Tree B and the distance "d" between Trees A and B are recorded.

If the nearest tree to this tree were chosen as the second member of the pair each time, the resulting distances would give a figure too small for the *average* distance between all trees in the woods.   Therefore an area around this first tree is excluded from consideration and any trees in this area are not chosen. This area is determined by the observer standing on the point and facing the nearest tree — A. Arms outstretched on either side of the observer mark a 180-degree angle. No trees in front of the observer in the 180-degree sector containing Tree A are chosen. Rather the nearest tree outside of this area *behind* the observer is chosen as the other member of the pair.

Its diameter and species are recorded, as is the distance between the chosen trees. With the use of a 180-degree angle, it has been determined that the distance must be multiplied by a correction factor of 0.8 to give the correct distance.

Procedure: A. Each pair proceed into the woods along the designated compass line and choose the first point so that it is well within the forest. Proceed to select the nearest tree and its pair by the technique described above, and record all necessary data.

      B. If the instructor has not designated the distance between points, choose a distance that will give trees not previously taken, and establish the second point.

      C. Take as many additional points as directed. (A minimum of 100 points per class should be taken for each stand.)

      D. Calculate the various quantities by the formulas below.

      E. List the species in order of importance values and compare with results from other methods if these are available for this study area.

The following formulas may be used to obtain analytic quantitative data:

1. Mean distance, $d = \dfrac{0.8D \text{ (Sum of all distances)}}{\text{Total number of distances taken}}$

2. Relative density $= \dfrac{\text{Number individuals of the species}}{\text{Number individuals of all species}} \times 100$

3. Relative dominance $= \dfrac{\text{Total basal area of the species}}{\text{Total basal area of all species}} \times 100$

4. Relative frequency $= \dfrac{\text{Number of points of occurrence of the species}}{\text{Number of points of occurrence of all species}} \times 100$

5. Mean area occupied by an individual $= (0.8d)^2$

6. Density or number of individuals per acre $= \dfrac{43560}{(0.8d)^2}$

7. Total basal area = Mean area × density (can be done for each species or all)

8. Importance value = Sum of quantities under numbers 2, 3, and 4 above

9. Frequency = $\dfrac{\text{Number of points of occurrence of the species}}{\text{Total points taken}}$

(Note difference between this and relative frequency.)

EXERCISE 29. Quarter method

Some data indicate that the quarter method is the best of the distance methods (Cottam and Curtis, 1956). It is of historical interest because of its similarity to the methods of the original Federal surveyors. The points are set up as in Exercise 28. Each sampling point is considered the center of four quarters, the predetermined compass

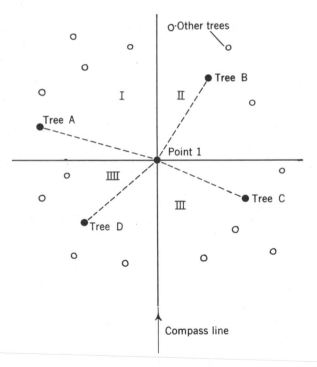

Figure 12.   The quarter method

The symbols I, II, III, and IV indicate the four successive quarters and A, B, C, and D the nearest trees to Point 1 in each quarter. The species and diameter of each of these four trees are recorded and the distance between each of them and the point.

line giving orientation (Figure 12). At each point the closest tree to the point in each of the quarters is chosen. The species and diameter of each of these four trees is recorded and then the distance between the *point* and each of the four trees is measured. The sum of these divided by four equals "d," the average distance. Refer to Exercise 28 for the analytic quantitative data that may be calculated. This method does not require the correction factor 0.8, which is therefore omitted wherever it appears in the formulas.

Procedure: A.   Each pair select points as in Exercise 28 and then proceed in the manner described above to select four trees per point, recording species, basal areas, and distances between the point and each of the four trees. A minimum of 100 points per class should be taken if time allows.

B.   Calculate all of the quantities as in Exercise 28.

C.   List species in order of importance values and compare with data from other methods if available. In large classes, part of the class can do Exercise 28 and the others this one for comparisons.

Part Four

Succession

One of the most fruitful concepts in ecology has been that of succession, the idea that the vegetation is dynamic and characterized by constant change (Cooper, 1926).

Succession that begins on bare denuded areas where there is no vegetation is known as primary succession. Secondary succession occurs when a normal succession is interrupted by some disturbance. So-called pioneer communities are replaced by others as the habitat changes until a more stable vegetation, more or less self-replacing, succeeds in establishing itself in what is called a climax.

CHAPTER 8 — SUCCESSION IN PLACE

The study of succession in place is most useful in forest studies, because it depends upon the determination of the relative sizes, and the relative numbers in these sizes, of the different species. The diameter of the tree is a rough indication of its age. Although the fact that different species grow at somewhat different rates limits the usefulness of this method, some idea of succession often may be obtained. For instance, if species "A" is represented by 100 trees of an average diameter of 24 inches and by 20 trees of an average diameter of 12 inches, whereas species "B" is represented by 20 trees of a diameter of 24 inches and 100 of 12 inches, a tentative conclusion might be that species B was replacing species A. Additional evidence of succession may be obtained by seedling counts, under the assumption that if the seedlings are the same as the dominant trees, the latter are climax, whereas differing seedlings may become the future climax. The method may be made more accurate by the actual determination of the ratio between age and diameter of the different species; this is done by counting the annual rings of cut stumps or of cores taken by increment borers.

EXERCISE 30. Determination of the ratio between age and diameter of trees

Procedure: A. The instructor will assign trees of the different species to different students. Each student take a core with the increment borer as follows: Insert the bit in the handle and remove the extractor. Punch the bit through the bark and then turn it gently until it reaches the center of the tree. Insert the extractor and then back off the borer about one turn to break the contact between the core and the tree tissue. The notch on the extractor should be up so that if the core breaks, it will be resting in the extractor. Pull out the extractor with the core. Immediately unscrew the borer so that it will not become frozen in the tree. Beginners will find cores of the conifers easiest to extract, count, and measure. Many hardwood cores are more difficult to read and must be mounted in wooden grooves with cement, then shaved smooth with a razor blade, and wet with water just before counting. Some experimentation with stains or dyes might be of interest and facilitate counting of rings.

    B. Count the rings and express the age of each tree in terms of its diameter. Average the data for the class for use in the following exercises.

EXERCISE 31. Tree counts by diameter classes

Procedure: A. Use the methods of Exercise 18 to collect the data for the designated study area, or use the data already collected.

    B. With meter sticks lay out a series of meter-square quadrats and count the tree seedlings by species (100 quadrats per class should be taken if time permits).

    C. Using the data from Exercise 30, express the relative numbers of each age group of the different species on a chart. If this data is not available, make a chart using diameter classes rather than age groups.

    D. Using the general principles mentioned above, make appropriate conclusions in regard to succession in this area.

CHAPTER 9 — SUCCESSION STUDY BY PERMANENT PLOTS

By far the best means of studying succession is permanent plots which can be observed over a period of years. Successive classes can benefit from the work of previous ones.

EXERCISE 32. Study of natural succession by permanent plots

In every area there are places in which the vegetation is changing. Obvious ones follow fires, landslides, and roadside excavations. Forests in which the seedlings of nondominant trees are most prevalent are probably changing. Rock faces and boulders provide a good opportunity to study early succession. Shores of small lakes or ponds frequently show signs of vegetation advance or retreat.

Precautions necessary in this type of study are the location of the sample plot so that it can be relocated and a system of marking its boundaries which is permanent and yet which does not in itself affect the succession. A single stake located from prominent features of the landscape by the methods of Exercise 2 may well be the best marker. The size of the plot is usually governed by the type of vegetation, for instance, approximately 0.1 meter square for low vegetation (mosses and lichens), 1.0 meter square for medium-sized vegetation (herbs and shrubs), and 10-meters square for tree-sized vegetation.

Procedure: A. Each pair select a sample plot of appropriate size in the designated succession area and drive a permanent iron stake to mark one corner of the area (circular areas may be circumscribed by considering the stake as the center of the plot).

   B. By compass bearings and measurements, locate this stake in terms of prominent landscape or other features.

   C. Make a careful record of the vegetation:
   1. If it is low vegetation, by the charting method of Exercise 23 or by overlays of plastic sheets for outlines of vegetation, for example, lichens or mosses.
   2. If it is other vegetation, by counting all the plants of each species and recording their sizes in diameter or height as appropriate.

3. By permanent photo stations if feasible.

D. From general observations of surrounding vegetation, make predictions for your sample plot.

E. If permanent plots have been previously established, locate them and recheck them in a manner similar to the former records.

F. Express any differences in table or graph form and make conclusions.

G. Suggest improvements to this experiment and carry them out if time permits and if so directed.

EXERCISE 33. Succession study of permanent denuded plots

It is sometimes convenient and desirable to denude plots artificially in order to study succession. The advantages of this technique include the possibility of a more convenient location and the opportunity to record the vegetation before denudation. The following exercise though directed for moss, lichen succession can be modified for use with higher plants.

Procedure: A. Each pair locate a patch of moss, lichen, or both. Carefully chart the vegetation in an area 4 centimeters square (see Exercises 23 and 24).

B. In the center of this area, clear down to the surface an area 2 centimeters square. If the edges of this square area are cut very precisely, regrowth will be observed more easily.

C. Carefully rechart any designated areas that have been established previously and indicate any succession that has occurred.

EXERCISE 34. Succession studies on artificially burned plots

In some areas, particularly where fires play an important part in the vegetation cover, as chaparral in California, or jack pine and aspen in the Lake States, fire-denuded plots are of great value. The actual burning of the area should be done by professionals and should be arranged through proper authorities in the area.

The advantages of set fires, other than that of location, are the opportunities to check the vegetation before and after and to set out instruments with which temperatures may be measured. Tempilaq (see Appendix A) that comes in different colors, melting at different temperatures, can be applied to asbestos squares normally used in the laboratory over Bunsen burners; these squares can be laid on the ground, buried to any depths, or attached on vertical poles to record temperatures reached at various places. Low poles suffice for grassland, but for forests it may be desirable to have poles as high as the trees.

Procedure before burning:

A. After arrangements for the burning have been made, each pair proceed as directed in some of the previous exercises to record the vegetation.

B. Each pair prepare ten asbestos squares by brushing on a series of Tempilaq spots each about an inch in diameter covering the range from 300 degrees to 1200 degrees Fahrenheit. Save one square for comparison after the fire and decide on the location of the other nine. Place buried ones with great care to avoid smearing the Tempilaq.

C. After checking these locations with the instructor, put them in position in the area to be burned.

D. Photographs of the area before, during, and after the fire are extremely useful.

E. Other projects may be devised, for instance, the collection of soil samples for seed germination tests before and after the fire.

Procedure after burning:

A. Check each of the asbestos squares and note that some of the Tempilaq spots have melted. Record the highest temperature one to be affected by the fire. This will indicate the temperature reached by the fire at this point. From your own and class data, make conclusions about the temperatures reached at different places.

B. Record the general appearance of the area and note any vegetation that may have survived. Dig out roots of various plants and record their condition.

C. Annually or at other intervals, check the vegetation by appropriate methods chosen from previous exercises, and make conclusions. If possible, over a long period of time, adjacent plots may be burned at intervals of five or ten years to provide a series of artificial succession stages from which future classes can benefit.

EXERCISE 35. Succession by exclusion plots

The problem of the effect of animals on plants can often be met by the use of exclusion plots. In principle, these are plots protected by fences or wire screens so that they may be compared with unprotected plots otherwise similar. In practice there is some difficulty in preventing the protective devices from affecting factors other than animals, for instance, wind and light. However, it is possible to use similar protective devices for two plots, with the exception that one of them includes openings for the animals; also possible is the setting up of inclusion plots as part of the series. Inclusion plots are those in which certain numbers and kinds of animals are placed inside an enclosure. The procedure will vary depending upon the area and animals being studied. The size of the quadrats should also vary with area and animals.

Procedure: A. Each pair set up devices to exclude the designated animals from a plot. If these devices seem to interfere with light or other factors, set up similar devices, on the control plots, but provide openings sufficient to admit animals.

   B. Record the vegetation by one of the methods designated from previous exercises. Note the general condition of the vegetation. Notes taken will depend upon the purpose of the study. Should the study be one of grazing in grasslands, the height, density, and species of vegetation would be of interest. If it is one of deer-browsing in a forest, the condition of the trees would be important to note.

   C. Recheck the vegetation at intervals. Some trapping might be useful in this study. If exclusion quadrats have been set out by previous classes, recheck these and make appropriate conclusions.

CHAPTER 10 — SUCCESSION STUDIES BY SURFACE PROFILES AND TRANSECTS

In some areas the land itself is constantly shifting with a consequent effect upon the vegetation. Such areas are those of sand dunes, river banks, and bogs. It is desirable in a study of these areas to maintain a record of the changing surface profile and the vegetation.

EXERCISE 36. Dune movement and vegetation transects

Although this exercise is written for sand dune studies, it can be modified for most erosional situations. The method consists in a transect (see Exercise 25) from a permanent stake at one end of the study area to a permanent stake at the other end. These stakes should, if at all possible, be placed in an area not subject to land movement. The beginning and end of the transect may be at some distance from these stakes provided that the ends are located by distance and bearing (see Exercise 2). It is better to proceed along a straight line, but if a change in direction is necessary, a stake should be placed at the point of divergence and the new direction indicated. This stake may be moved or covered by the shifting sand, but the spot can be relocated by distance and bearings.

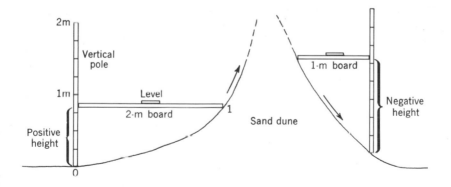

Figure 13.   Method of taking a surface profile

The surface profile is made by the use of two flat boards, a carpenter's level, and a vertical pole. In relatively flat areas, a board 2 meters long is used, whereas in steeper areas a 1-meter board is better. In practice the flat board is laid with one end on the ground at the higher side of the transect (see Figure 13). The other end is raised or lowered on the vertical pole until the carpenter's level indicates it is level. A surveyor's ranging pole, or any other 2-meter pole marked in centimeters, serves as the pole used to mark the vertical height of the profile at this point. As one proceeds up a slope, all heights are positive ones, and as one descends, these heights are negative and should be so marked. Note that upon descending, one places the vertical pole at the other side of the flat board.

Procedure: A. In teams of three or four, locate and set a permanent stake at or near the beginning of the designated transect-surface profile line. If it is necessary to begin other than at this stake, locate and set another stake at the beginning (see page 50).

  B. Proceed to record vertical heights as directed above, using the 2-meter or 1-meter board as appropriate. Record the presence of each species of plant in the 1- or 2-meter segments on forms as follows:

Distance	*Height*	*Vegetation*
0–1	+2	Ac, Bl, Or
1–2	+3	
2–3	−1	

If 2-meter lengths are used, the height and vegetation are recorded at the end of every 2-meters. Note that the distance along the ground will vary according to the steepness of the slope so that data will be based on sample plots of different sizes.

  C. Set a stake and locate the end of the line.

  D. Transfer the data to graph paper, using the distance from the form above on the horizontal axis and the height on the vertical axis. Place vegetation symbols on the graph at the appropriate places, and place a key to the symbols below.

  E. In subsequent years, relocate these transects or others done by previous classes and proceed as above. Construct a new profile and make a new record of the vegetation on the old graph in a different color to facilitate comparisons. Make conclusions concerning succession and the relative success of wind and vegetation in this area.

Part Five

Analytic Qualitative

Concepts

In previous analyses of vegetation we have been concerned with quantitative data, but there are aspects of vegetation for which qualitative judgement is significant. These concepts include sociability, vitality, periodicity, and stratification.

CHAPTER 11 — SOCIABILITY, VITALITY, PERIODICITY, AND STRATIFICATION

Sociability indicates the space relations of individual plants according to a scale, for instance, Braun-Blanquet (1932):

Soc. 1 = growing one in a place, singly

Soc. 2 = grouped or tufted

Soc. 3 = in troops, small patches, or cushions

Soc. 4 = in small colonies, in extensive patches, or forming carpets

Soc. 5 = in great crowds (pure populations)

There is an increasing use lately in America of the combined cover-abundance scale of Exercise 22 and of the sociability scale as a method of analyzing stands, even though other concepts of the Zurich-Montpellier School may not be followed (see Exercise 45). For instance, in jack pine studies in Michigan, the use of these scales in plots of a definite size, 10 meters by 20 meters, has proved valuable for following succession after controlled burning.

Vitality indicates the degree of prosperity of a species in the vegetation, whether it regularly completes its life cycle and produces seed, or not. A typical scale is that in Braun-Blanquet (1932):

Vit. 1 = Well developed, regularly completing the life cycle

Vit. 2 = Strong and increasing but usually not completing the life cycle (many mosses)

Vit. 3 = Feeble but spreading, never completing the life cycle

Vit. 4 = Occasionally germinating but not increasing; many ephemeral adventive plants

In studies according to Braun-Blanquet's (1932) system (see Exercise 22), a superscript "0" above and to the right of the figure for sociability is often considered sufficient indication of those species especially weak in vitality.

Periodicity expresses the rhythmic pattern in the life of the vegetation. Different investigators have used different abbreviations for this concept; these are often found in annotated lists of species. Typical symbols accompanied by the date of the study are found in Braun-Blanquet (1932):

fol. = in foliage

s.fol. = leafless

b. = buds

fl. = flowering

fr. = fruiting

sdl. = seedlings

ass. = assimilating (photosynthetic)

Stratification or layering refers to the vertical position of the various elements in the vegetation. Four principal layers may be recognized, each of which may be subdivided for special purpose studies: tree layer, shrub layer, herb layer, and moss layer.

EXERCISE 37. Determination of sociability, vitality, periodicity, and stratification

Procedure: A. Walk through the study area and indicate on the prepared species list, using the above scales and symbols, the sociability, vitality, periodicity, and stratification of those species assigned by the instructor. To save time, different species may be assigned to different students if the flora is rich in species.

B. Suggest modifications or additional symbols that would be better in your study area.

C. Describe the community in terms of these qualitative concepts.

Part Six

The Synthesis of
Data from Different Stands

The concrete analysis of particular stands of vegetation may be followed by the synthesis of data from many more or less similar stands. This synthesis may lead to an abstract concept of a community of some rank, to a vegetation spectrum in which each stand is assigned a relative position along a continuum, or to the concept of the nonexistence of plant communities. To some extent one's concept of the community is a function of the area studied and the degree to which an individual emphasizes the similarities or differences in stands.

The type of data taken, the methods used, and the manner of synthesizing it vary greatly; some of the aspects of synthesis are too advanced for an elementary class, but enough representative systems will be given to demonstrate the variation.

Some of these require data taken by a particular method already described in previous exercises. Others can utilize data taken by any method. Thus it is often possible to handle the same data in several different ways in the synthesizing of associations. [1]

Hypothetical associations and data may also be used to illustrate various facets of the problems involved. By this means some of the complications inherent in nature may be bypassed for the elementary student.

---

[1] The instructor may wish different parts of the class to do different ones of the following exercises, thus leading to class discussions concerning the different concepts.

If a class does not have data from enough stands for these exercises, papers may be assigned from ecological literature in which data on different stands is given, for instance, Roach (1952), Greig-Smith (1952), Tamm (1956), and Merkle (1951 and 1952). The bibliography lists ecological journals in which articles of this kind appear.

CHAPTER 12 — THE AMERICAN CLEMENTSIAN SYSTEM
(Weaver and Clements, 1938)

The concepts of Clements are used by many British and American ecologists. Communities are set up on the basis of dominants defined as the controlling species of the same life form, for instance, grasses in prairies and trees in a forest.

The major unit is the formation, considered a product of the climate. Formations are easily discernible without sampling and have already been established for many areas of study. In North America these include the Boreal Forest *(Picea-Larix)* Formation, the Prairie *(Stipa-Bouteloua)* Formation, the Woodland *(Pinus-Juniperus)* Formation, the Chaparral *(Quercus-Ceanothus)* Formation, and so forth (see Weaver and Clements, 1938).

Every climax formation consists of several associations: The Tundra *(Carex-Poa)* Formation consists of at least three associations, one of which is the *Carex-Cladonia* association. Associations are defined as plant communities with homogeneous physiognomy, ecological structure, and floristic composition.

Stands can generally be assigned to this kind of an association by a comparison of the results of samples indicating the abundance of and area covered by the species. Those species most abundant and of highest cover are the dominants, and stands with similar dominants are placed together in an association. Further observations on physiognomy, ecological structure, and floristic composition can also be useful in arriving at an abstract concept of the association.

The concepts of the climax dependent upon the climate and of a succession of stages of vegetation in a given climatic region to one climax community is central to the Clementsian monoclimax theory. Those associations in an area that are not climax are called "associes," indicating that they are in the succession series on the way to a climax.

Most ecologists today prefer the polyclimax point of view. This is the concept that the various associations of a region are a result not only of climate but also of the interaction of climate and physiographic, edaphic, pyric, and biotic factors.

The data from different stands over a period of years may be necessary for the succeeding exercises if not enough information is available from the year of study. This presupposes a minimum of change, so that data from rapidly changing stands should not be used in syntheses.

The instructor may wish to have some of the following data prepared before the class exercise.

EXERCISE 38. Determination of associations on the basis of the dominants

Procedure: A. Prepare a master list of the species in the various stands being considered, for instance, all the forest stands of a wooded area, or all the grass stands of a prairie.

B. After the list, in a series of columns, one for each stand, place the figures for the abundance (or density) and cover for each species in each stand in which it occurs.

C. From this master chart, extract those columns that have two or more dominant species in common, dominance being based on high abundance and cover of the dominant life-form layer. Place these similar columns in a series of separate charts, with the dominant species at the top. Some columns representing stands may have to be excluded until further stands are studied; columns with only one dominant species are saved for Exercise 39. Some judgment is necessary to decide which stands belong to the same association, and this must come with experience. The problem is to decide how high the abundance and cover should be for a species to be listed as dominant and how far below the leading dominant one should go for the second and successive dominants. Also there will be some variation in the figures for a particular species in the different stands. In general, in first setting up an association, only those stands should be considered that include some species with somewhat similar figures for abundance and cover. A blank column should be left at the end of these new charts for Exercise 42.

D. Describe the associations as established by their physiognomy, dominant species, and whatever similar ecological factors have been observed in the stands. How valid are these associations in your opinion? Compare these associations with those established by other methods, if results are available. Do all the stands have similar associated species? Try to explain any differences.

EXERCISE 39. Determination of consociations

Consociations are defined as subdivisions of associations locally controlled by single dominants.

Procedure: A. Place together in a chart those columns from the previous master chart that have the same species, and only one, as a dominant.

B. Indicate to what association these stands belong on the basis of Exercise 38 and the other associated plants in the stands.

C. Describe the various consociations on the basis of the several stands placed together.

D. Were there any observable environmental factors in these stands responsible for a consociation? Explain.

EXERCISE 40. The determination of societies

Societies are defined as communities within an association under local control of a subdominant; in a forest, for instance, shrubs, herbs, or mosses may be subdominant. Aspect societies are temporary seasonal phenomena, for instance, the local dominance of spring flowers in a desert or in a deciduous forest before leaves appear on the trees. A complete study of association composition should include sampling of the ground vegetation at different seasons. Layer societies are communities confined to one level of an association and are often studied separately, being divided into different communities with or without consideration of the other layers, for instance, the study of bark bryophyte communities (Phillips, 1951). The terminology for these communities is reviewed by Barkman (1958) and the consensus seems to be that these layer communities should be called "unions". They may be studied by adaptation of the previous exercises for each layer.

Procedure: *A.* Each pair make a study of the designated single layer and compare the relative place of each species with others in its layer. Frequency, abundance, or cover determinations may be directed.

B. Assemble the data from the same layer in as many stands as available and set up communities on the basis of dominance in that layer only. Follow the procedure of Exercise 38.

C. Do some of the same layer societies appear in different associations? Explain.

D. What, if anything, does the separate consideration of the layers add to your knowledge of the community?

CHAPTER 13 — A BRITISH SYSTEM OF DOMINANCE BY SCALES OF ESTIMATE

Many British ecologists set up associations on the basis of dominance determined by scales of estimate similar to those used in Exercises 15, 16, and 17. They believe that the study of associations requires a thorough knowledge of the flora and that subjective estimates based upon experienced judgment better express the vegetation than methods which may be more precise than necessary because of variation in the vegetation.

The following exercise makes use of data collected from many stands according to scales of estimate. Data collected by other methods that can be changed to scales of estimate may also serve as the basis for this exercise.

EXERCISE 41. Synthesis of associations according to dominance based on scales of estimate

Procedure: A. From class data taken in stands by scales of estimate or from the literature (articles in *Journal of Ecology*), each student make up a master table for the designated stands. Separate master tables should be prepared for obviously different vegetation, for instance, sand dunes, bogs, prairies, chaparral, forests, tundra, and so on.

B. In columns following the species in the master list, record the estimated figures (see Exercise 17) for the dominance of each species in each stand.

C. Make separate tables of those stands with similar dominant species. The number of dominant species in common that is necessary for inclusion of a stand is a matter of judgment. Generally, if many stands have numerous dominant species, then a stand with very few of these would probably be eliminated. Associations with many stands having few dominant species would include another stand with these few. Make separate tables for stands with only one dominant (consociations of Weaver and Clements, 1938). Leave a column at the end of all tables for Exercise 42.

D. Describe the associations set up on this basis. What is the role of species other than the dominants? If a series of associations has been established, what are their relationships to various observable ecological factors?

E. Compare the validity of these associations in comparison with those set up from the same general area by other methods.

CHAPTER 14 — PRESENCE

Presence is a measure of the regularity of distribution of a species in different stands of an association — that is, species of high presence occur in most stands of an association. Thus it is to stands of an association what frequency is to sample plots of one stand. Some Scandinavian phytosociologists prefer to use the term "segment-frequency," whereas the German word is "stetigkeit." If all of the stands being considered have been sampled with plots of the same area, then, when the number of stands containing a species is compared to the total number of stands, the resulting quantities are known as constancy. Presence differs from constancy by being calculated from stands in which the area sampled is different.

Presence is obtained when association tables are set up as in Exercises 38 to 41 inclusive. It may be expressed as a percentage by dividing the number of stands in which a given species occurs by the total number of stands and multiplying by 100, and then converted to the following scale (Braun-Blanquet, 1932):

$$1 = \ 1{-} \ 20 \text{ percent}$$
$$2 = 20{-} \ 40 \text{ percent}$$
$$3 = 40{-} \ 60 \text{ percent}$$
$$4 = 60{-} \ 80 \text{ percent}$$
$$5 = 80{-}100 \text{ percent}$$

EXERCISE 42. Use of presence in the synthesis of stand data

Procedure: A. Each student, using the association tables of previous exercises or other available data, calculate the frequency percentage for each species and place this figure in the last column of the table.

B. Discuss the significance of those species with high presence.

C. Explain any discrepancies between the relative importance of a species on the basis of presence and dominance.

D. In the setting up of associations, which seems more important, dominance or presence? Why?

EXERCISE 43. Use of constancy in the synthesis of stand data ("The Uppsala School" of Du Rietz, et al.)

Du Rietz (1930) and other exponents of the "Uppsala School" in Scandinavia use the concept of constancy in setting up associations. If similarly sized samples are taken from a series of stands that belong to one association, there should be a combination of several species with a high constancy percentage, that is, this combination occurs in most of the stands. The term "segment-frequency" is preferred by Du Rietz but here we will use "constancy". He believes that there is no fundamental difference between frequency of species in samples taken from one stand (segment) and constancy of species in several stands.

Thus the Uppsala School consider as an association a community in which combinations of species occur repeatedly. These species are not necessarily the dominant ones. In fact, for instance, in a forest region, associations on the basis of constancy are often composed of combinations of dominant trees with shrubs, herbs, or mosses.

Characteristic combinations of species can be set up on the basis of either presence or constancy, either from data taken by any of the analytical methods that indicate the presence or absence of species in the samples or from papers in the literature. The following exercise serves as the preliminary stage in the work of the "Zurich-Montpellier School" of Braun-Blanquet (1932, see Exercise 45).

A fine account of the manner in which associations are set up according to presence is in Knapp (1948). Although the book is in German, the tables can be consulted and understood by reference to the following exercises.

Procedure: A. Prepare a separate 4- by 6-inch card for each stand being considered, listing the species present followed by available data, for instance, abundance, cover, or frequency. Different students will be assigned different stands to facilitate card-making.

　　　B. It will then be possible on the basis of general observations to separate some of these cards into similar piles. This can be done on the basis of physiognomy, dominant species, life form, or ecological similarities of the habitats.

　　　C. Thumb through the cards in each pile and note repetitions of species combinations. Combinations may be underlined in different colors or otherwise marked to facilitate later identification.

　　　D. Place cards with similar combinations in the same piles to help build up the association tables. Students may be assigned different piles.

E. Next make a raw chart for each pile listing all the species on all the cards in a pile in a column at the left. Draw a series of vertical columns, one for each stand and in these columns place the available analytic data for each species in each stand. The number of species that is necessary in combination to form an association will vary. In a poor flora, three or four species may suffice whereas in a richer flora, nine or ten are better. Probably the more species that occur in repeatable combinations, the more valid is the association, within the limitations mentioned above. If many of the cards in one pile have, for instance, five species in common, a larger number have four species, and a fewer number have three, then those cards in the pile with only two species in common are probably fragmentary and should be discarded, at least at this preliminary stage. But if a large number of cards in one pile have only two species in common, then this number may be characteristic of this association.

F. In a column next to the end of the raw tables indicate the presence or constancy (see Exercise 42). Leave an additional column at the end for recording "fidelity" in Exercise 45.

G. Rearrange the raw table by placing those species with the highest presence or constancy at the top of the table. If two species have identical presence or constancy, place first that one with the higher figures in the majority of stands for the available analytical data. It is usual when making up this table to separate the different layers of vegetation. For special studies, any separation of the table is possible; grasses may be placed together, or bryophytes, and so forth.

H. After this smooth table has been established, it may be obvious that certain stands are sufficiently different to be excluded. For instance, a stand may have two of the combination species but all other associated species may be different from the other stands. Trial-and-error is necessary at this point, for with the elimination of stands, the figures for constancy or presence may change. Vertical columns may be cut out and pasted on other sheets. Horizontal strips may also be cut, if necessary, to change the position of species and eliminate others.

I. Describe each association on the basis of presence or constancy. Discuss the possibility that these associations are really lower categories of communities than those recognized on the basis of dominance.

EXERCISE 44. Recognition of sub-categories of associations

Once associations are established on the basis of presence or constancy, it is obvious that other species associated with the "characteristic" species vary in their role in the association. A consideration of these associates permits further subdivisions of these associations in the European sense.

This subdivision is accomplished by a study of the so-called "middle species," of neither the highest nor lowest presence, or sometimes by a study of those in the highest-presence classes that differ markedly from the others in vitality or dominance. Certain groupings of these "middle species" may occur in some of the stands and not in others. These species are called "differential" species.

Procedure: A. Using the assigned association table from Exercise 44 or the literature, make up a new table in which the species of middle presence are placed at the top of the table. Try to distinguish those stand columns that have similar groups of middle species and place these next to each other in the new table (see sample Table 5).

Table 5. Association table from which subcategories can be distinguished by groupings of middle presence or differential species (The last column "P" shows presence.)

STANDS

Species	1	2	3	4	5	6	7	8	9	10	P
A	x	x	x	x	x	x	x	x	x	x	5
B	x	x	x	x	x	x	x	x		x	5
C	x	x	x		x	x	x		x	x	5
D	x	x		x		x	x	x		x	5
E	x		x			x			x		3
F	x		x				x		x		3
G	x		x			x			x		3
H	x		x			x			x		3
I		x		x	x			x		x	3
J		x			x			x		x	3
K		x			x			x			2

From this table it is evident that the characteristic species of this association on the basis of high presence are Species A, B, C and D. The middle-presence species are E through K. To make the table suggested, Stands 1, 3, 6, and 9 would be placed in a separate table with Species E, F, G, and H at the top, followed by the others. Stands 2, 5, 8, and 10 would form another table. Stands 4 and 7 would be eliminated from subcategory consideration, but there might be present other species not here listed that would indicate their disposition.

The subdivisions erected on the basis of middle-presence species may be called subassociations, or variants.

If stands of these subdivisions have similar ecological factors, they are called subassociations. If all the stands in the south, for example, fall into one subdivision and those from the north into another, these subdivisions may be called geographical variants.

Some workers differentiate another subdivision, called a "facies," if the subdivision contains a species that is dominant and has high presence in the subdivision but a low presence in the rest of the association.

  B.   Study the data and observations from these subdivisions and record whether they are subassociations, variants, or facies.

  C.   Describe these subdivisions in terms of the "differential" species as they are called — that is, those species of middle presence that distinguish one subdivision of an association from others.

  D.   What is the purpose of this organization into subcategories?

EXERCISE 45. Synthesis of data by fidelity
(Zurich-Montpellier School of Braun-Blanquet, 1932)

Braun-Blanquet and his followers use the concept of fidelity to determine the "characteristic" species of an association. Fidelity is defined as exclusiveness or the degree to which species are confined to or do better in one or a few associations. The scale used is as follows:

A.   CHARACTERISTIC SPECIES

Fid. 5.   Exclusive species *(treue)*: species limited completely or almost completely to one community

Fid. 4.   Selective species *(feste)*: species found most frequently in a certain community but also, though rarely, in other communities

Fid. 3.   Preferential species *(holde)*: species present in several communities more or less abundantly but predominantly or with better vitality in one certain community

B.   COMPANIONS

Fid. 2.   Indifferent species *(vage)*: species without pronounced affinities for any community

Table 6.   Scheme for the determination of the fidelity of the species of a
            given association (Braun-Blanquet, 1932)

P = degree of presence; A = degree of abundance (Combined Scale, see
    Exercise 22)

Relationship of species with approximately the same vitality and sociability

In the given association	*In other associations*
Fidelity 5:	
P 4 to 5; A 3 to 5	P 1; A to 1
	P 1 to 2; A to 1
P 4 to 5; A + to 2	P 1; A + to 2
P 1 to 3; A any degree	Lacking or very rare
Fidelity 4:	
	P 2 to 3; A + to 2
P4 to 5; A 3 to 5	P 3 to 4; A + to 1 (as association
	relicts or pioneers)
P 4 to 5; A + to 2	P 2 to 3; A + to 1(2)
P 3 to 4; A + to 2	P 1 to 2(3); A + to 1(2)
P 1 to 3; A + to 2	P trifling; A very trifling
Fidelity 3:	
P anything; A 3 to 5	P + 3; A + to 2
P anything; A anything	P and A trifling or rather trifling or
	A trifling, vitality reduced
Fidelity 2:	
P, A and vitality in two or more	P, A and vitality in two or more
associations approximately equal	associations approximately equal
Fidelity 1:	
P 1; A + up to 1	P 1; A + up to 1
Vitality reduced	Vitality reduced
Species occurring only on the	Species occuring only on the
outskirts or on disturbed parts	outskirts or on disturbed parts
of the stand	of the stand

C. ACCIDENTALS

Fid. 1. Strange species *(fremde)*: species that are rare and accidental intruders from another plant community or relics of a preceding community

Fidelity of a species in a given association may be determined by Table 6.

To determine the fidelity for any species, it is first necessary to know all of the associations in an area in which this species might occur. Obviously then, the initial setting up of associations must be on some other basis.

Braun-Blanquet (1932) builds up associations on the basis of presence (see Exercise 42) and the analysis of stands by a combined scale of estimate (see Exercise 22). Presence is used instead of constancy because the size of plot necessary to sample a given stand is enlarged until all the "characteristic" species are present. This results in plots of different sizes in stands of the same association, although one of the criteria for the validity of an association is the amount of variation in size of plots necessary to sample a stand adequately. The more homogeneous the association is, the more uniform are the sample sizes and therefore the more closely presence resembles constancy.

Once the associations are established, it is soon evident that some of the species are restricted to one or a few associations and others occur in many associations. Species of high fidelity may be dominants, but often they are otherwise insignificant components of the vegetation, of low cover or abundance.

One of the great values of the concept of fidelity is the *recognition* of associations rather than their establishment. It is of great advantage in assigning a new vegetation stand to the correct association. These species correspond to "key" characters in plant taxonomy.

The concept of fidelity is also useful in checking on associations, and at this point the procedure becomes a trial-and-error process in which experience with the vegetation is paramount. Stands may be juggled back and forth on the basis of presence and fidelity, some added and some removed until the abstract concept of a particular association fits in to the pattern of the vegetation according to the considered judgment of the experienced observer.

This method may seem highly subjective, but it has resulted in some very detailed and monographic vegetation descriptions of great value.

Since the use of fidelity requires the work of many years in a given area, it is suggested that students be assigned journal articles that provide data that may be handled by the following exercise (see particularly articles in "Vegetatio") or given hypothetical association data.

Procedure: A. Each student prepare a table using a master list of all the species in an area. Use data from Exercise 42 or other data assigned. In the table with all species in a column at the left, make three vertical columns for each association of the area. For each species, place a figure in each association in which it occurs for presence, abundance, and, by reference to Table 6, fidelity.

      B. Place the figure for fidelity in the last column of the tables from Exercise 42.

      C. Does each association have species with high fidelity? Explain any discrepancies. Would you suggest rearranging the associations, disregarding some, or making new ones?

      D. Describe each association on the basis of its species of high fidelity.

      E. Do you consider this a useful concept? Explain.

CHAPTER 15 — THE CONTINUUM
(Curtis and McIntosh, 1951)

The synthesis of data from many stands within a given floristic province (defined as major units of vegetation consisting of formations and associations, for example, The Prairie Province, The Northeastern Coniferous Forest Province) has led some American ecologists to the concept of the *continuum*. They consider no two stands sufficiently alike to be associations, but rather as sufficiently different to be placed on a scale correlated with important environmental factors. For example, the moisture relationships of a forest may be such that stands can be found in varying degrees of wetness to dryness. A consideration of the quantitative analytical data from different stands of this forest from the continuum point of view results in an arrangement of stands in order from one extreme to the other with no two stands at exactly the same place on the scale. This is much like the spectrum of colors with its intergradation from one to the other and the consequent necessity of putting arbitrary limits to each color. It also recalls the difficulty of distinguishing certain species in the field of plant taxonomy.

Another facet of these investigations has been the attempt to select stands on an objective basis, for if only those stands are sampled that fit the investigator's preconceived idea of a homogeneous association, then his results will be biased. Thus the investigator may set up criteria in advance and take all stands that fit these; for instance, criteria from a recent study include "Natural forests of at least 15 acres in size, on upland land forms not subject to flooding and free from recent disturbance" (Brown and Curtis, 1952).

The quarter method of Exercise 29 is now recommended in place of the random pairs method of Exercise 28, for the analysis of individual stands, but any methods which give relative dominance (in terms of diameter-size), relative density, and relative frequency, or their equivalents, can be used. Those three values in percentages are added to give the importance value (I.V.), which adds to 300 for all the species in each stand (see Exercise 28).

In this way, the relative place of various species is based on three quantities instead of one.

The following description of the method is for a forest study but the principles can be and have been applied to other vegetation.

70

Summary data sheets are prepared for each stand investigated, giving the I.V. for each species. From the total list of trees of all stands are chosen the ones most prominent in at least one stand according to their I.V.

Next, a table is prepared in which the average I.V. of the trees in stands dominated by the leading dominants are placed (see sample Table 7).

Table 7. Average importance value (I.V.) of trees in stands, with given species as leading dominants

Number of Stands	Leading Dominant	Spp A	B	C	D	E	Climax Adaptation Number
25	Spp. A	150	25	21			1
20	B		152				2
10	C			50			2
	D		etc.				2
	E						3
	F						4

The first column indicates the number of stands of all those studied in which the species in the second column are the leading dominants. The figures in the body of the table are the importance values of the species listed across the top. For instance, Spp A was the leading dominant in 25 stands and in these had an I.V. of 150 (sum of relative frequency, density, and dominance; see Exercise 28). In the 25 stands dominated by Spp A, Spp B had an I.V. of 25, and Spp C an I.V. of 21.

Referring to Table 7, species A in the 25 stands it dominates has an average I.V. of 150 (sum of I.V. in each of the 25 stands, divided by 25) whereas species B has an average I.V. of 25 in these same stands.

The order in which the leading dominants are arranged is decided by some noted relationship to the environment, in terms, perhaps, of pioneer species versus climax ones. So in Table 7, species A represents the most nearly climax and species E the most nearly pioneer. Another check on the order is a trial-and-error placement until both horizontal and vertical columns most nearly approach a smooth curve on a graph.

71

When the order is established, a climax adaptation number is assigned to each species, with ten for the climax ranging down to one for the pioneer species. Subdominant tree species are assigned numbers on the basis of their close association to one of the dominants. Different trees may have the same climax adaptation number (see Table 7).

In order to put each stand in its proper position along a continuum, the I.V. of each species in the stand is multiplied by its climax-adaptation number; the sum of these products gives the continuum index (C.I.). This will vary between 300 and 3,000 for each stand. For instance, see Table 3 in Brown and Curtis (1952), partially reproduced here as Table 8.

Table 8. Partial adaptation from Brown and Curtis's (1952) Table 3 entitled "Original data for importance values of 17 species and for three soil characteristics"

Stand Number	C.I.	Spp. A	B	C	D	E	F	G
084	356	272	4	9		12		4
066	375	237	46	7	6		5	
068	467	etc.						

Referring to Table 8, stand number 066 has species A with an I.V. of 237 and a climax adaptation number of 1 so 237 × 1 = 237; species B had an I.V. of 46 and a climax adaptation number of 2, so 46 × 2 = 92; species C had an I.V. of 7 and a climax adaptation number of 2, so 7 × 2 = 14; species D had an I.V. of 6 and a climax adaptation number of 2, so 6 × 2 = 12; and species F had an I.V. of 5 and a climax adaptation number of 4, so 5 × 4 = 20. The sum of 237, 92, 14, 12 and 20 equals 375, the continuum index (C.I.) of stand 066.

Behavior of individual species can be checked by making graphs with the I.V. of that species on the vertical axis and the stands arranged according to their continuum indices on the horizontal axis.

Segregation of the C.I. into 100-unit segments and averaging of the I.V.'s for species helps to reduce the information further, and if this is smoothed by a moving average formula it is even more useful. For example, from Brown and Curtis (1952), the average I.V. of *Acer saccharum* in the 100-segment stands from C.I. 2,490 to 2,590 is 92, from 2,510 to 2,610, 95, and from 2,500 to 2,600, 93. Their formula for a moving average is on the following page:

$$B = \frac{n_1 a + 2n_2 b + n_3 c}{n_1 + 2n_2 + n_3} \,,$$

where B is the smoothed value of b and n_1, n_2, n_3 = number of stands included in averages a, b, and c. Thus,

$$B = \frac{100 \times 92 + 200 \times 93 + 100 \times 95}{100 \quad + 200 \quad + 100} = 68 \pm$$

When a graph is drawn with this data for the leading species — that is, with stands arranged according to C.I. on the horizontal axis and average I.V. of the species on the vertical axis — one obtains a series of smooth curves in which the high points of each indicate their maximum importance and present a composite picture of the relationships of the trees to each other.

According to the advocates of the continuum concept, this method fails to indicate the existence of separate communities but does indicate "that all stands studied are parts of a community complex, arranged along a gradient from pioneer conditions of low moisture, high light, low soil organic matter, and low soil base content to climax conditions of medium moisture, low light, high soil organic matter, and high base content" (Brown and Curtis, 1952). No two major species have their optima in the same range, nor do any of the species appear to form groups in the same range.

EXERCISE 46.   Synthesis of data leading to a continuum

Procedure: A.   Each student take the assigned data from a series of stands of the same life form and proceed as above to make tables and calculate the required quantities leading to importance values, climax adaptation-numbers, and continuum indices.

      B.   Arrange the stands in order of their continuum indices.

      C.   Compare this treatment of stands with other treatments available for your area. Do you think the vegetation of your area is better considered as a continuum or in associations? Why? Under what circumstances might one interpretation be more desirable than the other?

CHAPTER 16 — VEGETATION FORMULAS
(Stamp, 1929, and Gates, 1942)

One of the problems of comparing the various stands of communities and also of comparing different communities is the establishment of a clear visual presentation. Reduction of the data to simpler yet accurate terms is the goal in devising vegetation formulas.

A published vegetation formula (Stamp, 1929) is as follows:

$$300 \; A^d \; a \, b \, x \; (20) + 50 \; F^d \; y + 1000 \; (2Hz + 10G \; m \, n \, o \, z')$$

The figures before the capital letters indicate the number of individuals per hectare, the capital letters indicate the different layers: A = trees, F = shrubs, H = herbs, G = grass, and C = cryptogams. Additional letters, or A', F', and so forth, are used if subdivisions of these layers or other layers seem desirable. Exponents indicate general characteristics: d = deciduous, e = evergreen, and so on. Each of the small letters, such as a, b, and x, stands for an individual species: the key to them should be placed below the formula. Dominant species are underlined. The numerals in parenthesis following each layer indicate the height of the vegetation.

In the future, other formulas using other quantitative data either analytical or synthetic may prove of value.

EXERCISE 47. Devising vegetation formulas

Procedure: A. Devise a new and different formula that can be used to present any of the class data collected to date. Carefully explain the symbols used and present the data from at least two stands or two different communities for comparison.

B. Alternatively, modify Küchler's (1949) physiognomic classification (see Exercise 6) to a formula by placing appropriate figures before the letters. These figures may include any desired quantity obtained by any of the methods of the previous exercises in any of the stands studied.

C. Using the formulas from several stands of the same association, discuss the variation found. Does this support the concept of associations in your opinion? Construct a composite formula for the association based on the formulas of individual stands.

CHAPTER 17 — THE DEGREE OF MATURITY OF A PLANT COMMUNITY (Pichi-Sermolli, 1948)

In previous discussions on succession in Part IV, the idea of a series of different communities developing successively in an area, leading to a climax community, was set forth. Some criteria were mentioned for the recognition of climax communities.

Pichi-Sermolli (1948) suggests an index for the establishment of the maturity in plant communities based on the frequency percent of all species in the stands of a community. The principle is the long-accepted notion that the higher the frequency percent of each species and the smaller the number of sporadic species, the more mature is the community.

The index is obtained by adding the frequency percent of all the species in a stand, on the basis of twenty-five 0.1-square-meter plots, for instance, and dividing this sum by the total number of species in the stand. All the other stands of the community are then considered and the index of maturity of each compared to establish the general maturity of the community (see Table 9).

Thus the maturity index for these four stands is similar. The nearer to 100 the index of maturity is, the more mature the community.

An index of maturity may be figured for any community for which frequency data is available.

EXERCISE 48. Establishing an index of community maturity

Procedure: A. Take the frequency figures for as many stands as directed of a given community and calculate a maturity index for this community.

B. Compare these maturity indices with those of other members of the class.

C. Compare the relative maturity of any stand with available climax data from succession studies of Part IV.

D. Does the maturity index correspond with impressions, observations, or other data regarding the place of this community in the succession series? Explain.

Table 9. Maturity index for four stands of a hypothetical community (based on Pichi-Sermolli, 1948)

Spp.	Stands			
	1	2	3	4
A	100	70	70	
B	90	80	100	100
C	80	60		80
D			80	60
E	70	40	10	70
F				30
G	40	50	90	
H				45
I	30	65	50	
J				50
K	10			
L				64
Total Spp. Frequency	420	365	400	500
No. of Spp.	7	6	7	8
Maturity Index	60	61	59	65

The figures in the table are the frequencies of each of the species in the four different stands. These are totaled for each stand and divided by the number of species in each stand to arrive at a maturity index which may be compared with that of other stands.

CHAPTER 18 — COMMUNITY COEFFICIENTS
(Jaccard, 1912)

Another way in which stands may be compared to find out whether or not they belong to the same community is by community coefficients. These are mathematical expressions of similarities of species. Community coefficients can also indicate the degree of resemblance of two communities.

In practice, species lists of the two stands or two communities are drawn up. In a table, the species are placed in a left-hand column with three columns following. Column one is for species of community or stand A, column two for species common to both, A and B and column three for species of community or stand B.

In these columns may be placed the occurrence (Jaccard, 1912), the frequency (Gleason, 1920), or the frequency percent (Kulczynski, 1937, in Oosting, 1956). Somewhat different formulas are used to arrive at an index. Quantities other than frequency may be experimented with; for instance, cover values may be significant in expressing similarities between stands and communities.

The index is usually obtained by adding the figures in column one, then in column two, and then in column three. One-half of the total of column two is divided by the sum of the totals of column one, one-half of column two, and column three. This figure is then multiplied by 100.

Kulczynski's (1937) formula as given by Oosting (1956) is

$$\frac{2w}{a + b} \times 100$$

"w" is the sum of the lower of each pair of percentages in column two, and "a + b" is the sum of all percentages in columns one and two.

EXERCISE 49. The determination of community coefficients

Procedure: A. Procure the data for two stands thought to be similar to each other and two others thought to be different from each other.

B. Calculate the community coefficient in accordance with the directions above by consideration of the occurrence of species.

C. Now calculate the coefficient or index by whatever other data are available, and by the use of these formulas or others you can devise.

D. Which method and what data do you prefer and why?

E. Devise a new system by summing several different quantities, for instance, the importance value of Exercise 28. Is this a better indication of similarities and differences than the use of a single quantity? Why?

CHAPTER 19 — THE STUDY OF COMMUNITIES ON THE BASIS OF PERCENTAGE DENSITY, FREQUENCY, BASAL AREA, AND SIZE CLASSES
(Oosting, 1942, and Billings, 1938)

Many American ecologists sample stands on the basis of quadrats (originally square sample plots) of 100 square meters for trees, 16 square meters for shrubs, 1 square meter for herbs, and 1/4 square meter for bryophytes. These quadrats are usually distributed as widely as possible throughout the stand along lines parallel to the long axis of the stand and a predetermined distance apart. The different-sized quadrats are nested, with the smaller ones set in a corner of the larger.

In the tree and shrub quadrats the following are taken: density (see Exercise 13) changed to percent of total density (dividing the density of a given species by the total density of all species and multiplying by 100); frequency (see Exercises 7 to 10) changed to frequency percentage; basal area changed to percentage basal area (equals relative dominance); and, for trees, the percentage of the different size classes present in each species.

Four categories may be chosen according to height: overstory, understory, transgressives, and seedlings, or, alternatively, diameter-size classes used, for instance, 0 to 3, 3 to 6, 6 to 12, 12 to 24, and over 24 inches diameter at breast height, plus a seedling class. The number of individuals of each species in each category in the quadrats is counted.

From tables summarizing these data, bar graphs or phytographs may be constructed (Oosting, 1956). Phytographs provide graphic representation of the different quantities, here four in number (see Figure 14).

In Figure 14, this particular tree species has 60 percent of the total tree density, 70 percent frequency, occurs in 100 percent of the size classes, and has 50 percent of the total basal area. When phytographs are published, the scale is usually omitted.

In herb quadrats, the density and frequency of species is often indicated (see Exercises 13 and 7 to 10).

For the synthesis of tree data, a table is made with the species in a column to the left; in vertical columns for each stand, data concerning the species in that stand are placed. Density and frequency data are generally used.

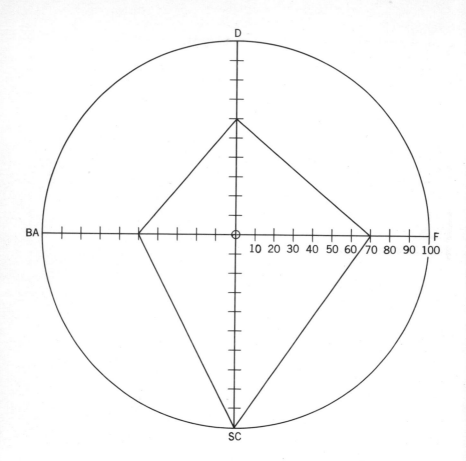

Figure 14.   Phytograph for a tree species
Each radius is marked from 0-100 percent

OD   = percentage of total tree density
OF   = frequency percentage
O-SC = percentage of size classes of the species
O-BA = percentage of total basal area

For the synthesis of herb data, the frequency percents of a species in all of the stands in which it occurs are added, and the sum is divided by the number of stands for one "summation value." The density of a species in each of the stands is added and the sum multiplied by a figure to express density in terms of number of individuals per 1000 quadrats or 1000 square meters. For instance, if five stands of ten quadrats each are tallied, with a consequent total density of 6.2 for the 50 quadrats, multiplying by 20 (1000 divided by 50) results in a figure of 124 as the second "summation value" in terms of number of individuals per 1000 square meters.

Thus the relative importance of the different tree, shrub, and herb species in a given community can be ascertained.

EXERCISE 50. Community studies combining density, frequency, basal area, size classes, and summation values

Procedure: A. The instructor will designate the location of a minimum of ten quadrats as directed above.

B. Each pair locate and lay out a 10-by-10-meter quadrat by stakes and ropes. In one corner lay out a quadrat 4 by 4 meters, and in a corner of this a 1-by-1-meter quadrat. If so directed, sample the moss layer by a 1/4-square-meter plot.

C. Record data for the smaller quadrats first to avoid trampling effects. For the moss layer, use one of the methods of Part IV, if directed. For the herb layer, record density and frequency of the species in the 1-square-meter plots. For the shrubs, record counts by height classes in the 4-by-4 meter plots. In the large plots, set up diameter classes for the trees (see Exercise 18), and take data for the four quantities mentioned above.

D. Total the class data, then each student construct tables and phytographs as appropriate for the presentation of these data. Certain species may be assigned to different students for the phytographs.

E. Write a description of this community on the basis of this stand.

F. If other stands of this community have been analyzed, make tables for the different layers with columns for each stand as suggested above. Calculate and record summation values. If a series of stands of different ages are being studied, relationships and successions may be shown by putting the stands in order in these tables with the youngest ones to the left. Stands can also be placed in order by a consideration of any other factor, for instance, moisture.

CHAPTER 20 — THE STUDY OF FOREST ASSOCIATIONS ON THE BASIS OF PERCENTAGE CANOPY COMPOSITION IN LONG TRANSECTS
(E. Lucy Braun, 1935 and 1950)

In extensive investigations in the deciduous forests of eastern North America, Braun has used percent of canopy composition from samples taken on long transects to delineate communities. Surface profiles may be sketched or made from topographic sheets, if available. Strata other than that of trees were observed, and lists were made of the species, together with general notes on the important ones.

For instance, the forests of Pine Mountain, Kentucky (Braun, 1935), contain thirty-four canopy species of which sixteen attain an important position in one or more of the forest types. Associations composed of these species show considerable range in composition and constituent species as well as in the dominance of these species from place to place, and so the term "association-segment" (Braun, 1950) is proposed for these variants.

To obtain percent of canopy composition, all the trees reaching into the canopy are counted by species; for each species, its total number divided by the total number of all trees in the sample and multiplied by 100 gives its percent composition.

Synthesis of the data from these samples is presented in a large table with associations and association-segments in a column at the left followed by a series of vertical columns, one for each tree species. In the body of the table is placed an "X," indicating the occurrence of species in the particular association-segment. Dominants are indicated by a heavy X, important species by a lighter X, and all others by an x. The selection of the symbol is based partly on the composition lists and partly on additional field notes. Thus can be determined the community range of any particular species, some ranging through many and others restricted to fewer communities. For instance, dominants of the most xeric communities are likely to be absent or very unimportant in the mixed mesophytic communities, and so forth.

EXERCISE 51. Community studies by transects sampled at intervals for percentage canopy composition

Procedure: A. Each pair run a long transect of several miles, preferably crossing several communities, recording obvious shifts from one community to another, and tentatively selecting areas which should be sampled on the return trip. The sampling areas should be well within a community — that is, not near or in a transition zone. Notes, in order, should include trees encountered with a rough idea of dominance and whatever time permits concerning shrubs and herbs. The instructor may designate the study of trees alone.

B. On the return trip, sample the trees of each of the different recognizable communities in a belt 100 meters long and 2 meters wide. In a column at the left of your notebook, list the species as encountered and record after each species the number of individuals in the belt. Count and record only those individuals that extend into the canopy.

C. Calculate the percentage of canopy composition for each tree species as explained above. On the basis of these percentages and field notes, assign to each species a symbol in each stand indicating whether it is dominant, important, or merely present.

D. Prepare a master table of all the communities sampled and indicate the relative position of each species in these communities as suggested above.

E. Draw a rough map of the area, indicating the communities and their boundaries.

CHAPTER 21 — THE STUDY OF COMMUNITIES BY THE USE OF CONTIGUOUS QUADRATS
(Greig-Smith, 1952a, b, and c)

The intriguing question of whether species are dispersed randomly, regularly, or clumped may be examined to some extent by the use of contiguous quadrats (see Greig-Smith, 1952a, b, and c). These are sample plots touching one another and arranged in a grid (Exercise 11). The data from these plots may be summed in many different ways to indicate adequacy of sampling. When all data are added from all plots, a total census of the area involved is available for comparison. Any combination of plots or blocks of plots, or any distribution of plots, can be chosen and summation data compared with the total census. If statistical treatment of the data is desired, the Greig-Smith references should be consulted. The whole problem of quantitative plant ecology is well-discussed in Greig-Smith (1957).

The area available may be enlarged by successive classes and used for other exercises.

EXERCISE 52. Sampling by contiguous quadrats

Procedure: A. The first pair set out a line of the designated length, for instance, 100 meters or more in forests, and drive in a permanent stake at either end. The second and successive pairs set their lines a designated width from the previous pair's line (10 meters in forests); the last pair set two lines.

B. Beginning at one end of their two lines, each pair place two strings parallel to each other and between the lines to form a square for the first quadrat. Successive quadrats can be set by moving the rear string forward.

C. Record the occurrence of each species on a data sheet in which the species are in a column to the left followed by a series of columns, one for each quadrat and a final column for frequency.

D. Summarize the frequency data for the class; in this instance, with ten pairs there would be 100 plots, a desirable minimum.

E. Different pairs will then be assigned the calculations for different combinations of quadrats. These can include data from ten plots chosen at random; from a diagonal group of ten plots; from a vertical column and a horizontal column of ten plots; from different numbers and locations of groups of two or more plots together to simulate larger plot sizes; from every other plot, and so on.

    F. Compare the data obtained from the designated combination with the summarized class data. Make conclusions in regard to the adequacy of your sample.

    G. If so directed, check this data statistically.

CHAPTER 22 — STUDY OF COMMUNITIES BY CORRELATION COEFFICIENTS

Another useful method of setting up associations from the analysis of stands is the determination of correlation coefficients (see deVries, 1954, Cole, 1949, Greig-Smith, 1952a, b, and c, and references in these papers).

This method is based on the idea that associations are composed of species that should occur together often. Thus a correlation coefficient can be assigned to two species on the basis of their occurrence or nonoccurrence together. If two species always occur together, the correlation coefficient, designated as "r," equals plus 1. If these species never occur together, r equals minus 1.

The computation of r is a mathematical problem, the solution of which requires a thorough understanding of statistics, but for our purposes here, the formulas will be presented without a detailed explanation of their derivation. Reference to Snedecor (1956) can be made by interested students. The method used by deVries (1954) in grassland studies in the Netherlands will be described as an example.

DeVries chose homogeneous grassland stands and sampled them by walking two diagonals and taking a handful of grass at the end of the

	Y		
X	A	B	P = A + B
	C	D	Q = C + D
	R = A + C	S = B + D	N P + Q and R + S

- A = No. times X and Y occur together
- P = No. times Y occurs in total
- R = No. times X occurs in total
- P − A = B = No. times Y occurs without X
- R − A = C = No. times X occurs without Y
- D = No. times X nor Y occur at all
- N = Total no. samples
- S = N − R = B + D
- Q = N − P = C + D

Figure 15. Contingency table for use in determining correlation coefficients of species (adapted from deVries, 1954) toe a predetermined number of paces apart to get 100 handfuls per hectare. Frequency data were calculated as well as occurrence for each species.

Using a 2 by 2 contingency table (Figure 15), in which the vertical and horizontal columns add in both directions, r is figured by the following formulas.

$$r = \sin (T \times 90°),$$

where,

$$T = \frac{AD - 3C}{\sqrt{P \times Q \times R \times S}}$$

DeVries considers r unreliable if R or P is lower than thirty, which means that if one of the species occurs less than thirty times in the samples, the correlation coefficients should not be calculated for those species.

In practice, one determines A, P, R, and N, and from these determines the other quantities necessary by reference to Figure 15. The mathematical calculations can usually be turned over to the mathematics department for the determination of r between the most common species. It is suggested that the instructor designate a limited number of species for this preliminary exercise.

Although negative correlations are important in indicating antagonisms or different habitat tolerances of species, we will consider here the further treatment of positive correlations only.

Species with r values close to zero "do not care much with which species they grow" (deVries, 1954).

Tables are now constructed with the species listed in a column at the left and the same species in a horizontal line at the bottom and

Table 10. Correlation coefficients times 100 for certain species pairs (adapted from deVries, 1954)

	Ar	Av	D	Fr	Gv	Tri
Ar						
Av	63					
D	74	63				
Fr	60	42	8			
Gv	57	60	31	60		
Tri	68	68	61	28	60	
Species	Ar	Av	D	Fr	Gv	Tri

with correlation coefficients between the species in the body of the table. The correlation coefficient r is usually multiplied by 100 for use in the table (see Table 10).

From this type of table, which is adapted from a small part of deVries (1954), are set up constellations as in Figure 16.

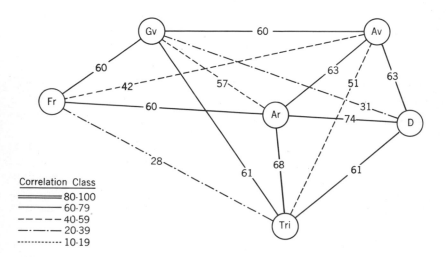

Figure 16. Constellation of plants from Table 10 (adapted from deVries, 1954)

The correlation coefficients from Table 10 are used to arrange the species in this figure. For instance Spp. Ar in the center has a high correlation coefficient with each of the others, whereas the coefficient between Fr and Tri (placed somewhat farther apart) and between Fr and D is much lower: 28 and 8, respectively.

The constellation figure is constructed by locating species with high correlation coefficients in the same general vicinity and, by a trial-and-error process, adjusting positions so that a given species is correctly placed according to its positive correlations with all other species in the table.

DeVries recognized some communities similar to those of Braun-Blanquet (1932), but was able to see many more connections between species, leading him to the conclusion that plant communities conceived as combinations of species are sharply limited in nature.

Interesting habitat relationships were also revealed by constellation figures. For instance, in deVries's (1954) Figure 2, the upper part of the chart contained drought-enduring species, the extreme right lime-loving, the extreme left acid-loving, and the lower part, species that occur in areas not too wet nor too dry.

It should be added that deVries is aware of the importance of dominance and frequency as well as of combinations of species in the establishment of communities.

EXERCISE 53. Constructing a constellation figure from correlation coefficients

The basic data for this exercise can be obtained from any samples of many similar stands that contain information as to the occurrence or nonoccurrence of different species together in the samples. DeVries (1954) used 1000 analyses of grasslands all over the Netherlands. This number will seldom be available for class use, but the principle can be understood and the method practiced with any number available.

Procedure: A. Each student take the assigned data and proceed as above to construct a constellation figure of the leading species on the basis of their correlation coefficients times 100.

B. Can you discover any relationship between communities established by other methods and the position of species in your constellation figure? Explain.

C. Discuss any discovered relationship between position of species in the constellation diagram and observable habitat factors.

CHAPTER 23 — REDUCTION OF SAMPLING ERROR BY STRATIFICATION OF THE SAMPLE
(Brown, 1954)

Sampling error occurs because no sample that is smaller than the total area can be absolutely accurate. As an example, if a 1000-acre area contained 100,000 trees, and was sampled by ten plots of 1/10 of an acre each, each of the 1/10-acre plots would give a number of trees that could be expressed in terms of trees per acre. In the total plot there would be 100 trees per acre, but in sample one there might be 95 trees per acre, in sample two, 105 trees per acre, and so on. Thus sample one would be five trees per acre wrong (100 − 95 = 5). This is called the sampling error. Although the error cannot be calculated in every instance, an average error over a large number of samples can be calculated. Mathematical calculation is facilitated by use of "standard error," not a straight average but the square root of the mean of the squares of the individual errors. The mean is the total sum of the squares divided by one less than the total number of squares.

Random sampling error can be reduced by increasing the size of the sample or, with smaller sample sizes, increasing the number of units. It can also be reduced by stratifying the sample, the object of this exercise.

EXERCISE 54. Sample stratification

Sample stratification is useful in areas that can be divided into parts uniform within themselves, but differing from other parts. If the whole study area is homogeneous, stratification is unnecessary. If the study area is on a slope, however, or if one section is wetter than another or had a different history, then stratification can be of value.

Procedure: A. Each pair in the designated area distribute sample plots by random tosses within a uniform stratum. Repeat this for each of the different strata in the area. Different pairs may be directed to do different strata to save time. Record abundance of each species in each quadrat separately (or use any other directed quantity).

B. Summarize the data in tables or graphs in two different ways:

(1) Separately by strata
(2) All samples together for the whole area.

C. Make comparisons and conclusions.

CHAPTER 24 — SYNTHESIS OF DATA ON THE BASIS OF SCATTER DIAGRAMS
(Anderson, 1949)

Anderson (1949) states that the human mind is inefficient in judging variation in more than one variable at a time. This definitely limits us in synthesis of data from stands to form an abstract concept of an association, since the component species are variable in many quantities and qualities. Therefore the use of scatter diagrams affords a new possibility of data presentation that is pictorial and that enables the human mind to make these more complex comparisons.

Scatter diagrams are the simple alignment of dots in a two-dimensional field and, according to Anderson (1949), are superior to correlation coefficients for population analysis. They may well be superior also for community analysis.

One system is hereby presented, but the student is encouraged to devise other quantities and qualities which may be even better for community synthesis and also analysis. Figure 17 indicates a sample scatter diagram and key for a hypothetical community.

The two circles in Figure 17 represent stands that may or may not be in the community being studied. That is, the stand's inclusion in the community may be determined by its position and other characteristics. Lines radiating from the dots indicate the other characteristics as described in the key.

The stands in Figure 17 are being considered in terms of the frequency index community coefficient (see Exercise 49) and the average species percentage cover according to the scale of Trepp (1950; see Exercise 17). For instance, Stand 1 in the table below the scatter diagram has nine species of different cover percentage. These are averaged to give a value for the stand of 41 percent, or a scale number of three. Its frequency index community coefficient is 80, and so it is plotted thus on the diagram. Radiating lines indicate its average density percentage, habitat moisture conditions, and soil pH, an indication of soil acidity. Stand 2 is also plotted, as an example of a stand with low FICC and average coverage percent. No attempt is made here to consider all of the relationships which may be brought out by these diagrams, but reference can be made to Anderson (1949) for further ideas. The data for phytographs of Exercise 19 might be expressed as pictorialized scatter diagrams, to include even more data in one figure.

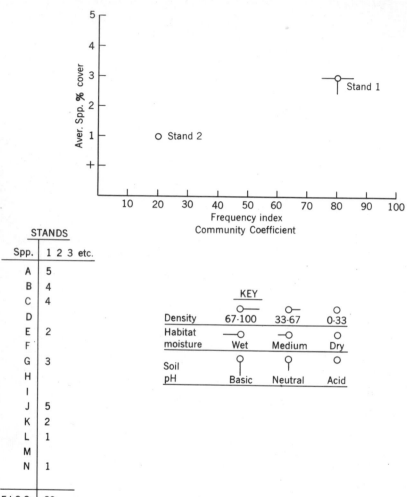

Figure 17. Pictorialized scatter diagrams for stand synthesis
Each circle represents a single stand of a community. Lines radiating from the circles indicate characteristics described in the key.
Frequency Index Community Coefficients are calculated for each
stand and plotted against the Average Species Percentage Cover
to give the position of each circle. A valid abstract community
concept can be synthesized if many circles are located in the same
area of the diagram.

EXERCISE 55. Scatter diagrams for community synthesis

Procedure: A. Each student select from the data on various stands assigned as many qualities and quantities as are available on some scale basis.

        B. Construct a key to these quantities and qualities and a pictorialized scatter diagram similar to Figure 15 for these stands.

        C. Discuss the relative place of these stands in the vegetation.

        D. Does this system reveal any relationships not previously revealed? Explain.

Part Seven

Artificial Populations

CHAPTER 25 — CONSTRUCTION AND USE OF ARTIFICIAL POPULATIONS

The analysis of the adequacy of samples is a study in itself. Some of the previous exercises have been designed to show the effect of sample size, number, and distribution results. These exercises were done on field populations for which we had little information as to the type of dispersal of the plant species. The species can be distributed at random, regularly like an orchard, or clumped. Different sampling methods are adequate for different distributions.

Many of these problems can be solved best by the setting up of artificial populations on charts, in which the species can be distributed and sampled as desired. This is somewhat comparable to the field of plant physiology in which plants are subjected to artificial conditions in the laboratory, and the same precautions hold, namely, that simultaneous natural field experiments are desirable.

In practice, a large chart (see Cottam, Curtis, and Hale, 1953) 1 meter square can be gridded, as in Exercise 11. Heavy lines are drawn for every 10-centimeter square and lighter lines for each 1-centimeter square. Using one millimeter as the finest unit, there are one million points available, and even if 1000 species individuals are distributed, the available area is more than adequate. Any number of individuals can be chosen for dispersal in any manner. Random dispersal can be accomplished by reference to random numbers tables (Exercise 11, IBM cards; see Cottam, Curtis, and Hale, 1953) or more easily by scattering different-colored discs by hand (see Greig-Smith, 1952a). Regular dispersal of individuals can be accomplished along reference lines evenly distributed throughout, whereas clumped dispersals can be made by randomly distributing a number of clump centers and scattering different numbers of individuals at random at these centers. For clumped distributions, Greig-Smith (1952a) determined the number of individuals to be randomly dispersed at each center from a Poisson series with a mean of four and determined the actual position by placing a card cylinder 20 centimeters in diameter over each center, and dropping the associated discs into it.

Once these three different dispersion charts are made, the discs are glued on and ozalid copies produced. These copies can be used for the indoor performance of many of the previous exercises, using samples of different sizes and shapes as well as different distributions. Cardboard or plastic sample plots of different sizes and shapes can be made and placed on the chart in a manner simulating field work and those species recorded that are covered by the sample plots. For instance, frequency, abundance, and, if different-sized discs are used to simulate different-sized plants, cover can be obtained.

To prepare a more natural chart, it may be desirable to distribute different species in different ways, some randomly, some clumped and some regular. An evaluation of the different sampling methods may be obtained by analysis of how well each samples these different species on the same chart. Since a record is available of the actual numbers distributed, comparisons can be made between sample and actual. The construction of charts can be a class project, but since it is time-consuming, it is somewhat preferable to have it done by assistants, if they are available. Examples of excellent chart construction can be found in Curtis (1956). Those students with statistical training will find that much of this type of data lends itself to statistical treatment. Reference can be made to Snedecor (1956) or Cochrane (1953).

For random dispersal of sample plots, an overlay gridded in inches is suggested as better than the same grid with which the species were dispersed. A sample exercise is described below.

EXERCISE 56. Artificial populations

Procedure: A. The instructor will assign different methods for each pair to use on the designated chart copy. For instance, if the chart is simulating a forest stand, one group will be assigned the random pairs method (Exercise 28), another the quarter method (Exercise 29), another the Bitterlich method (Exercise 27), and so on, using numbers and distributions of points as suggested in those exercises.

B. Prepare a chart in which you compare your data with the previously prepared total data. How adequate is your sampling method?

C. Compare your method with the methods used by others in the class.

D. How do these results compare with available field results using the same methods?

BIBLIOGRAPHY

LITERATURE CITED

Acocks, J., *Veld Types of South Africa,* Bot. Survey Mem. No. 28, Dept. Agri., Div. Bot., Pretoria, Union of South Africa, 1953.

Anderson, E., *Introgressive Hybridization.* New York: John Wiley and Sons, Inc., 1949.

Barkman, J., *On the Ecology of Cryptogamic Epiphytes.* The Hague: Nederlandse Organisatie voor Zuiver-Wetenschappelijk Onderzoek', 1958.

Beard, J.S., Climax Vegetation in Tropical America. *Ecology,* 25: 127-158, 1944.

Billings, W., The Structure and Development of Old Field Short-Leaf Pine Stands and Certain Associated Physical Properties of the Soil. *Ecol. Monog.,* 8: 437-499, 1938.

Blackman, G.E., A Study by Statistical Methods of the Distribution of Species in Grassland Associations. *Ann. Bot.,* Lond., 49: 749-777, 1935.

Bormann, F.H., The Statistical Effect of Plot Size and Shape in Forest Ecology. *Ecology,* 34: 474-487, 1953.

Braun, E. Lucy, The Vegetation of Pine Mountain, Kentucky. *Amer. Midl., Nat.,* 16: 517-65, 1935.

————, *Deciduous Forests of Eastern North America.* The Blakiston Co., Philadelphia, 1950.

Braun-Blanquet, J., *Plant Sociology.* (Trans., rev., and ed. by G.D. Fuller and H.S. Conard.) New York: McGraw-Hill Book Co., 1932.

Brown, Dorothy, *Methods of Measuring Vegetation.* Commonwealth Agricultural Bureau. Bucks, England, 1954.

Brown, R., and Curtis, J., The Upland Conifer-Hardwood Forests of Northern Wisconsin. *Ecol. Monog.,* 22: 217-234, 1952.

Buell, M.F., and Cantlon, J.E., A Study of Two Communities of the New Jersey Pine Barrens and a Comparison of Methods. *Ecology,* 31: 567-586, 1950.

Cain, S., The Species-Area Curve. *Amer. Midl. Nat.,* 19: 578-581, 1938.

————, A Biological Spectrum of the Flora of the Great Smoky Mountains National Park. *Butler Univ. Bot. Studies,* 7: 1-14, 1945.

Canfield, R. Application of the Line Interception Method in Sampling Range Vegetation. *J. For.,* 39: 388-394, 1941

Cochrane, W., *Sampling Techniques.* New York: John Wiley and Sons, Inc., 1953.

Cole, L., The Measurement of Interspecific Association. *Ecology,* 30: 411-424, 1949.

Conard. H., *The Background of Plant Ecology.* Ames, Iowa: Iowa State Press, 1951. (A transl. of *"The Plant Life of the Danube Basin,"* by Anton Kerner, 1863).

Cooper, W.S., The Fundamentals of Vegetational Change. *Ecology,* 7: 391-413, 1926.

Cottam, G., and Curtis, J.T., A Method for Making Rapid Surveys of Woodlands by Means of Pairs of Randomly Selected Trees. *Ecology,* 30: 101-104, 1949.

————, Correction for Various Exclusion Angles in the Random Pairs Method. *Ecology,* 36: 767, 1955.

————, The Use of Distance Measures in Phytosociological Sampling. *Ecology,* 37: 451-460, 1956.

———— and Hale, B., Some Sampling Characteristics of Randomly Dispersed Individuals. *Ecology,* 34: 741-757, 1953.

Curtis, J., *Plant Ecology Workbook.* Minneapolis: Burgess Publishing Co., 1956.

———— and McIntosh, R., An Upland Forest Continuum in the Prairie-Forest Border Region of Wisconsin. *Ecology,* 32: 476-496, 1951.

Dansereau, P., *Biogeography, an Ecological Perspective.* New York: The Ronald Press, 1957.

————, A Universal System for Recording Vegetation. *Contr. de l'Institut Bot. de l'Univ. de Montreal,* 72: 1-58, 1958.

Davis, T.A.W., and Richards, P., The Vegetation of Moraballi Creek, British Guiana: an Ecological Study of a Limited Area of Tropical Rain Forest. *J. Ecol.,* 21: 350-384, 1933.

DeVries, D., Constellation of Frequent Herbage Plants Based on Their Correlation in Occurrence. *Vegetatio,* 5-6, 105-111, 1954.

DuRietz, G., Vegetationsfurschung auf soziationsanalytischer Grundlage. *Handb. der biol. Arbeitsmeth.,* teil 5 heft 2. Abderhalden, 1930.

Gates, F., The Bogs of Northern Lower Michigan. *Ecol. Monog.,* 12: 213-54, 1942.

Gleason, H., Some Applications of the Quadrat Method. *Torrey Bot. Club Bull.,* 47: 21-33, 1920.

Goode, J.P. and Espenshade, E.B., Jr., *Goode's School Atlas, Physical, Political and Economic.* New York: Rand-McNally Co., 1950.

Greig-Smith, P., The Use of Random and Contiguous Quadrats in the Study of the Structure of Plant Communities. *Ann. Bot., N.S.,* 16: 293-316, 1952a.

————, Ecological Observations on Degraded and Secondary Forest in Trinidad, British West Indies. I. General Features of the Vegetation. *J. Ecol.,* 40: 283-315, 1952b.

Greig-Smith, P., Ecological Observations on Degraded and Secondary Forest in Trinidad, British West Indies. II. Structure of the Communities. *J. Ecol.,* 40: 316-330, 1952c.

————, *Quantitative Plant Ecology.* New York: Academic Press, Inc., 1957.

Grosenbaugh, L.R., Plotless Timber Estimates-New, Fast, Easy. *Jour. Forestry,* 50: 32-37, 1952.

Handbook of Physics and Chemistry. Chemical Rubber Publishing Co., 2310 Superior Ave., N.E., Cleveland, Ohio.

Jaccard, P., The Distribution of the Flora in the Alpine Zone. *New Phytol.,* 11: 37-50, 1912.

Kerner. *See* Conard.

Knapp, R., Arbeitsmethoden der Pflanzrnsoziologie. *Verlagsbuchhandlung Eugen Ulmer in Stuttgart,* z. Zt. (14a) Ludwigsburg, Kornerstr. 16, 1948.

Kuchler, A.W., A Physiognomic Classification of Vegetation. *Ann Ass. Amer. Geog.,* 39: 201-210, 1949.

Levy, E.B., and Madden, E.A., The Point Method of Pasture Analysis. *N.Z.J. Agri.,* 46: 267-279, 1933.

Loveless, A.R., and Asprey, G.F., The Dry Evergreen Formations of Jamaica. *J. Ecol.,* 45: 799-822, 1957.

Merkle, J., An Analysis of the Plant Communities of Mary's Peak, Western Oregon. *Ecology,* 32: 618-640, 1951.

————, An Analysis of a Pinyon-Juniper Community at Grand Canyon, Arizona. *Ecology,* 33: 375-384, 1952.

Oosting, H., An Ecological Analysis of the Plant Communities of Piedmont, North Carolina, *Am Midl. Nat.,* 28: 1-126, 1942.

————, *The Study of Plant Communities.* W.H. Freeman and Co. San Francisco. (2nd Edition), 1956.

Penfound, W., A Study of Phytosociological Relationships by Means of Aggregations of Colored Cards. *Ecol.,* 26: 38-57, 1945.

Phillips, E., The Associations of Bark-Inhabiting Bryophytes in Michigan. *Ecol. Monog.* 21: 301-316. 1951.

Pichi-Sermolli, R., An Index for Extablishing the Degree of Maturity in Plant Communities. *J. Ecol.,* 36: 85-90, 1948.

Raunkiaer, C., *The Life Forms of Plants and Statistical Plant Geography; being the Collected Papers of C. Raunkiaer.* Clarendon, Press, Oxford, England, 1934.

Roach, A., Phytosociology of the Nash Crater Lava Flows, Linn County, Oregon. *Ecol. Monog.,* 22: 169-193, 1952.

Snedecor, G., *Statistical Methods.* The Iowa State College Press, Ames, Iowa, 1956.

Stamp, C., Vegetation Formula. *Nature,* 123: 833-834, 1929.

Tamm, C., Composition of Vegetation in Grazed and Mown Sections of a Former Hay Meadow. *Oikos,* 7: 144-157, 1956.

Tansley, A.G., and Adamson, R.S., Reconnaissance in the Cotteswolds and the Forest of Dean. *J. Ecol.*, 1: 81-89, 1913.

Trepp, W., Ein Beitrag zu Bonitierungamethoden von Alpweiden. Schweiz. landw. Mh. 28: 366-371, 1950.

Weaver, J., and Clements, F.E., *Plant Ecology* (2nd Edition). New York: McGraw-Hill Book Co., 1938.

BOOKS FOR CLASS USE

Braun, E. Lucy, *Deciduous Forests of Eastern North America.* The Blakiston Co., Philadelphia, 1950.

Braun-Blanquet, J., *Plant Sociology.* (Trans., rev., and ed. by G.D. Fuller and H.S. Conard.) New York: McGraw-Hill Book Co., 1932.

Brown, Dorothy, *Methods of Measuring Vegetation.* Commonwealth Agricultural Bureau. Bucks, England, 1954.

Cain, S., *Foundations of Plant Geography.* New York: Harper and Brothers, 1944.

Conard, H., *The Background of Plant Ecology.* Ames: Iowa State Press, 1951. (A transl. of *"The Plant Life of the Danube Basin,"* by Anton Kerner, 1863).

Dansereau, P., Biogeography, an Ecological Perspective. New York: The Ronald Press, 1957.

Daubenmire, R., *Plants and Environment.* New York: John Wiley and Sons, 1947.

Gates, F., *Field Manual of Plant Ecology.* New York: McGraw-Hill Book Company, 1949.

Geiger, R., *The Climate Near the Ground.* (Transl. by M. Stewart et al of "Das Klima der Bodennahan Luftschicht".) Cambridge, Massachusetts: Harvard University Press, 1950.

Good, R., *The Geography of the Flowering Plants.* Longmans, Green and Co., London, 1947.

Greig-Smith, P., *Quantitative Plant Ecology.* New York: Academic Press, Inc., 1957.

Handbook of Physics and Chemistry. Chemical Rubber Publishing Co., 2310 Superior Ave., N.E., Cleveland, Ohio.

Harshberger, J., *Phytogeographic Survey of North America.* New York: G.E. Stechert and Company, Inc., 1911.

Kittredge, J., *Forest Influences.* New York: McGraw-Hill Book Co., 1948.

Kramer, P., *Plant and Soil-Water Relationships.* New York: McGraw-Hill Book Co., 1949.

McDougall, W., *Plant Ecology* (Fourth edition). Philadelphia: Lea and Febiger, 1949.

Oosting, H., *The Study of Plant Communities.* W.H. Freeman and Co., San Francisco. (2nd Edition), 1956.

Schumacher, F., and Chapman, R., Sampling Methods in Forestry and Range Management, *Duke University School of Forestry Bull.* 7, (rev. ed.). Durham, N.C., 1948.

Sears, P., *Life and Environment.* New York: Teachers College, Columbia University, 1939.

Shantz, H., and Zon, R., The Physical Basis of Agriculture: Natural Vegetation. *Atlas of American Agriculture,* Pt. I, Sect. E., Washington, D.C., U.S. Department of Agriculture, 1924.

Shelford, V. (editor), *Naturalists' Guide to the Americas.* Baltimore: Williams and Wilkins Co., 1926.

Snedecor, G., *Statistical Methods.* The Iowa State College Press, Ames, Iowa, 1956.

Trewartha, G., *An Introduction to Weather and Climate.* New York: McGraw-Hill Book Co., 1954.

U.S. Department of Agriculture. *Soils and Men.* Gov.Printing Office,Washington, D.C., 1938

U.S. Department of Agriculture. *Climate and Man.* Gov. Printing Office, Washington, D.C., 1941.

Weaver, J., and Clements, F.E., *Plant Ecology* (2nd Edition). New York: McGraw-Hill Book Co., 1938.

ECOLOGICAL JOURNALS

(In approximate order of usefulness in the United States.)

Ecology. Ecological Society of America and Duke Univ. Press, Durham, North Carolina.

Journal of Ecology. British Ecological Society and Blackwell Sci. Publications, Oxford, also Charles C. Thomas, Publ. Springfield, Illinois.

Vegetatio. International Review of Plant Sociology. Uitgeverij Dr. W. Junk, Den Haag, Holland.

Butler University Botanical Studies. Dept. of Botany, Butler University, Indianapolis, Indiana.

American Midland Naturalist. University of Notre Dame, Notre Dame, Indiana.

Oikos. Ecological Journal of Denmark, Finland, Iceland, Norway and Sweden. Ejnar Munksgaard, Publishers, Copenhagen, Denmark.

Forest Science. A Quarterly Journal of Research and Technical Progress. Society of American Foresters, Washington, D.C.

Ecological Monographs. Ecological Society of America (for longer papers) and Duke Univ. Press, Durham, North Carolina.

OTHER JOURNALS WITH SOME ECOLOGICAL ARTICLES

American Journal of Botany

Annals of Botany

Botanical Gazette

Botanical Review

Biological Abstracts

Bulletin of the Torrey Botanical Club

Cambridge Philosophical Society Biological Reviews

El Aliso of the Rancho Santa Ana Botanical Garden, Claremont, California

Evolution

Geographical Review

Journal of Agricultural Research

Journal of Agricultural Science

Journal of Forestry

Madrono of the California Botanical Society, Berkeley, California

The New Phytologist

Planta

Plant Physiology

Review of Canadian Biology

Soil Science

Svensk Botanisk Tidskrift

APPENDIX

A. CLASS INSTRUMENTS AND EQUIPMENT

1.   Abney level. No. N5710P is suggested with scales of degrees and percent of grade (rise or fall in 100 feet on the horizontal.) The Keuffel and Esser Co. Manual on Abney levels suggests additional uses.

2.   Adding machine or calculator.

3.   Compass, Brunton-type pocket transit on tripod with swivel-joint head. A minimum of two is needed.

4.   Increment borer. One 12 inches long and one 18 inches long are desirable.

5.   Pantograph.

6.   Tempilaq. Available from 113 degrees Fahrenheit to 1500 degrees Fahrenheit from Tempil Corp., 132 W. 22nd St., New York 11, New York. Can be purchased in liquid or pellet form.

B. STUDENT INSTRUMENTS AND EQUIPMENT

Quantities necessary from the following list depend upon the number of people in each group. Some exercises are better for individuals, others for pairs or larger groups.

1.   Binder twine or kite string. Lengths as needed for cross-ropes in gridding.

2.   Bitterlich sticks. Built of wood as shown in Figure 10; angle prisms now available from forestry suppliers are less bulky but no better for most woods.

3.   Boards, flat 3/4 by 3 inches, 1 meter long and 2 meters long, for Exercise 36.

4.   Calipers, inside-outside, marked in inches and millimeters, for Exercise 19.

5.   Discs, paper. Number, sizes, and colors as needed for Exercise 56.

6.   Fences or screens as needed for exclusion quadrats in Exercise 35.

7.   Knife, pocket.

8. Level, carpenter's, for Exercise 36.

9. Meter sticks, marked in centimeters and inches. Basal area or some other desired scale may be added. Forestry cruising sticks may be desired by some, marked in various quantities.

10. Notebook, 8½ by 11 inches, with aluminum covers, and notebook paper with a broad column at left followed by narrower data columns.

11. Pins, surveyors. 18 inches long, pointed, red and white.

12. Protractor, celluloid or plastic, for Exercise 2 and other mapping.

13. Point frame apparatus, of wood or light metal as shown in Figure 8, for Exercise 26.

14. Ranging pole or stadia rod. See Stadia rods.

15. Ropes, clothesline, or sash cord. Lengths as needed; desired divisions can be marked by inserting colored cloth or string between strands or by using nail polish.

16. Ruler, plastic. Marked in centimeters on one side and inches on the other.

17. Sample plots, small plastic or cardboard, of different sizes and shapes for Exercise 56.

18. Square frame of light metal framework bolted at ends with wing nuts for easy disassembling; of different sizes as necessary. Other shapes can be made for special studies.

19. Squares of clear plastic, 1 centimeter square, and other sizes as needed.

20. Stadia rods or redwood boards, 3/4 by 3 inches, 3 meters long (can be made folding). Marked in centimeters with 10-centimeter segments painted alternating red and white.

21. Stakes, permanent, of iron pipes in needed lengths. Painted tops will aid in location of stakes.

22. Stakes, wooden, as an aid in establishing temporary points, in sizes as needed.

23. Stick and radius string.

24. Tapes, steel. Marked in feet and inches on one side and meters and centimeters on the other. Tapes 30 meters or 100 feet in length are most useful, although some prefer shorter ones.

INDEX

random numbers tables 22
random pairs method 42 ff
Raunkiaer, C. 11, 19
Richards, P. 13
Roach, A. 57

sand dunes 53
sample distribution 22
sample numbers 20
sample shape 21
sample size 21
scatter diagrams 91
segment-frequency 62, 63
Snedecor, G. 22, 86, 96
sociability 55 ff
societies 60
species-area curve 20
square frame 21
Stamp, C. 74
standard error 90
Stetigkeit 62
stick and radius rod (or string) 19
stratification 55 ff
    of sample 90
subassociations 66

succession, 47 ff
summation value 81
surface profile 53
synecology xv
synthesis of data 57 ff

Tamm, C. 57
Tansley, A.G. 26
temperature determination, in fires 51
Tempilaq 50
transects 38, 53, 82
transitions in vegetation 38
tree counts 26, 48
    height 11
Trepp, W. 29, 91

unions 60

variants 66
vegetation xv
vegetation formula 74
vitality 55 ff

Weaver, J. 58, 61

Zurich-Montpellier School 55, 66